KT-222-796

The Oxford Book of Children's Poetry

MANCHESTER CITY LIBRARIES	
C0009189645	
Bertrams	21/12/2009
J821.008	£14.99

OXFORD
UNIVERSITY PRESS

Great Clarendon Street, Oxford OX2 6DP
Oxford University Press is a department of the University of Oxford.
It furthers the University's objective of excellence in research, scholarship,
and education by publishing worldwide in

Oxford New York

Auckland Cape Town Dar es Salaam Hong Kong Karachi
Kuala Lumpur Madrid Melbourne Mexico City Nairobi
New Delhi Shanghai Taipei Toronto

With offices in

Argentina Austria Brazil Chile Czech Republic France Greece
Guatemala Hungary Italy Japan Poland Portugal Singapore
South Korea Switzerland Thailand Turkey Ukraine Vietnam

Oxford is a registered trade mark of Oxford University Press
in the UK and in certain other countries

This selection and arrangement © Michael Harrison and Christopher Stuart-Clark 2007

Illustrations for *What Is Poetry?* copyright © 2007 Tem Doran
Illustrations for *My Life* copyright © 2007 Maddy McClellan
Illustrations for *Off to School* copyright © 2007 Adam Stower
Illustrations for *There Isn't Time!* copyright © 2007 Peter Bailey
Illustrations for *If I Were Lord of Tartary* copyright © 2007 Niroot Puttapipat
Illustrations for *I Think I Could Turn and Live with Animals* copyright © 2007 Chris Mould
Illustrations for *Earth, Earth, Under My Shoe* copyright © 2007 Paul Howard
Illustrations for *I Am the Song* copyright © 2007 Inga Moore

The moral rights of the authors have been asserted

Database right Oxford University Press (maker)

First published 2007

All rights reserved. No part of this publication may be reproduced,
stored in a retrieval system, or transmitted, in any form or by any means,
without the prior permission in writing of Oxford University Press,
or as expressly permitted by law, or under terms agreed with the appropriate
reprographics rights organization. Enquiries concerning reproduction
outside the scope of the above should be sent to the Rights Department,
Oxford University Press, at the address above

You must not circulate this book in any other binding or cover
and you must impose this same condition on any acquirer

British Library Cataloguing in Publication Data

Data available

ISBN: 978-0-19-276276-4

1 3 5 7 9 10 8 6 4 2

Printed in China

Paper used in the production of this book is a natural,
recyclable product made from wood grown in sustainable forests.
The manufacturing process conforms to the environmental
regulations of the country of origin.

The Oxford Book of Children's Poetry

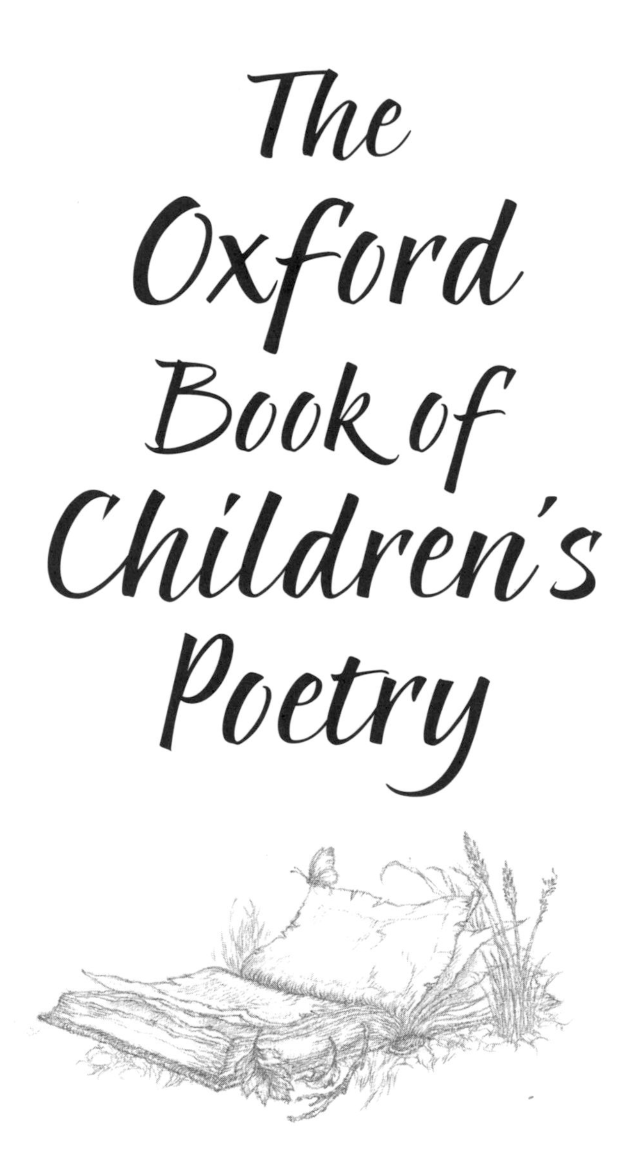

Michael Harrison &
Christopher Stuart-Clark

OXFORD
UNIVERSITY PRESS

Contents

What is Poetry?

My Life

Off to School

There Isn't Time!

If I Were Lord of Tartary

I Think I Could Turn and Live with Animals

Earth, Earth, Under My Shoe

I Am the Song

What Is Poetry?

Poetry

What is Poetry? Who knows?
Not a rose, but the scent of the rose;
Not the sky, but the light in the sky;
Not the fly, but the gleam of the fly;
Not the sea, but the sound of the sea;
Not myself, but what makes me
See, hear, and feel something that prose
Cannot: and what it is, who knows?

ELEANOR FARJEON

Alphabet Stew

Words can be stuffy, as sticky as glue,
but words can be tutored to tickle you too,
to rumble and tumble and tingle and sing,
to buzz like a bumblebee, coil like a spring.

Juggle their letters and jumble their sounds,
swirl them in circles and stack them in mounds,
twist them and tease them and turn them about,
teach them to dance upside down, inside out.

Make mighty words whisper and tiny words roar
in ways no one ever had thought of before;
cook an improbable alphabet stew,
and words will reveal little secrets to you.

JACK PRELUTSKY

Sound Advice

Once you write a poem
You must write another

To prevent the first
From falling over.

ROGER MCGOUGH

New Poem

So far, so good

ROGER MCGOUGH

What is Pink?

What is pink? A rose is pink
By the fountain's brink.
What is red? A poppy's red
In its barley bed.
What is blue? The sky is blue
Where the clouds float through.
What is white? A swan is white
Sailing in the light.
What is yellow? Pears are yellow,
Rich and ripe and mellow.
What is green? The grass is green,
With small flowers between.
What is violet? Clouds are violet
In the summer twilight.
What is orange? Why, an orange,
Just an orange!

CHRISTINA ROSSETTI

The Secret Rhyme for Orange

Where's the secret rhyme for Orange?
Is it lurking somewhere near?
Go and look under the sofa.
No? There's only grey fluff there?

Then where is that stupid rhyme?
I've been looking now for days!
Searching through the dictionary
Is like searching through a maze.

How can a word have no rhyme?
It really is not funny,
Orange is not a lonely word—
It's always seemed quite chummy.

You'd think if a word had no rhyme
It would be one like 'Grim' or 'Bad',
Not a juicy word like Orange—
It really makes me mad.

Look amongst the leaves of the Orange tree.
See if the rhyme's sleeping there
Curled up in the branches
Without a worldly care.

Look in the caverns of the Sun,
Look on Jupiter and Mars.
If they've got a rhyme for Orange
Bring it back. It's ours.

BRIAN PATTEN

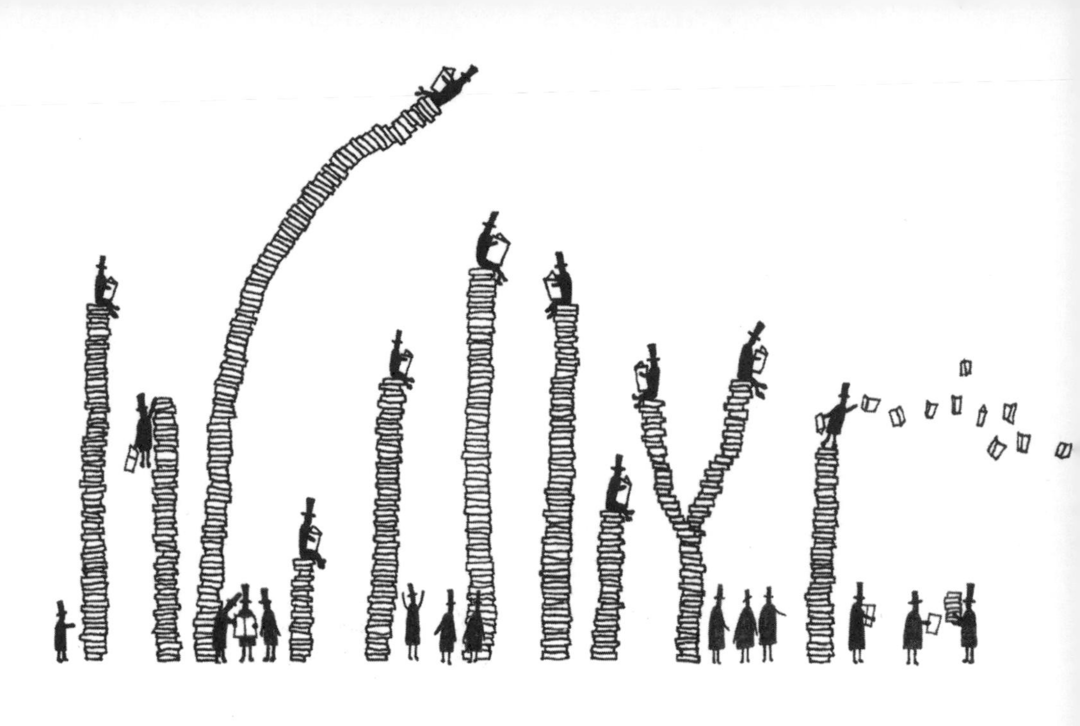

W

The King sent for his Wise Men all
  To find a rhyme for W;
When they had thought a good long time
  But could not think of a single rhyme,
'I'm sorry,' said he, 'to trouble you.'

JAMES REEVES

I Saw Esau

I saw Esau sawing wood,
And Esau saw I saw him;
Though Esau saw I saw him saw,
Still Esau went on sawing.

ANON.

Hlep!

Something has gone wrog in the garden.
There are doffadils blooming in the nose-beds,
And all over the griss dandeloons
Wave their ridigulous powdered wigs.

Under the wipping willop, in the pond
Where the whiter-lollies flute,
I see goldfinches swamming
And the toepaddles changing into fargs.

The griss itself is an unusual shade of groon
And the gote has come loose from its honges.
It's all extrepely worlying!
Helg me, some baddy! Heap me!

And it's not unly in the ganden.
These trumbles have fellowed me indares.
The toble has grown an extra log
And the Tally won't get Baby-See-Too.

Even my trusty Tygerwriter
Is producing the most peaqueueliar worms.
Helg me, Sam Biddy. Kelp me!
Helg! HOLP! HELLO!!

GERARD BENSON

Mr Bidery's Spidery Garden

Poor old Mr Bidery.
His garden's awfully spidery:
Bugs use it as a hidery.

In April it was seedery,
By May a mass of weedery;
And oh, the bugs! How greedery.

White flowers out or buddery,
Potatoes made it spuddery,
And when it rained, what muddery!

June days grow long and shaddery;
Bullfrog forgets his taddery;
The spider legs his laddery.

With cabbages so odoury,
Snapdragon soon explodery,
At twilight all is toadery.

Young corn still far from foddery
No sign of goldenrodery,
Yet feeling low and doddery

Is poor old Mr Bidery,
His garden lush and spidery,
His apples green, not cidery.

Pea-picking *is* so poddery!

DAVID MCCORD

As I Went Down the Cat-Walk

As I went down the cat-walk
   Where all the catkins blow,
I saw an old cat-burglar
   Beside a cattalo.
And O he miaowed and O he mewed
   Just like the cat-bird's call.
I said, 'Pray cease this catalogue
   Of scatty caterwaul.
I didn't catch your name, I fear,
   But how, my dear old chap,
Among such cataracts of tears
   May I take my cat-nap?'
He said, 'Of various cat-calls
   I'm running the gamut
Because upon my cat-fish
   No catsup has been put!
Such catchpenny behaviour
   It makes me ill, then iller.'
I said, 'Please don't excite yourself.
   Lean on this caterpillar.'
I plucked from off the apple tree
   A juicy, ripe cat's-head.
He took it with some cat-lap
   And felt much better fed.
And then he played cat's-cradle
   And turned cat in the pan,
And sailed to Catalonia
   All in a catamaran.
He sailed away by Catalan Bay
   That happy cataman.

CHARLES CAUSLEY

Sir Smashum Uppe

Good afternoon, Sir Smashum Uppe!
We're having tea: do take a cup!
Sugar and milk? Now let me see—
Two lumps I think? . . . Good gracious me!
The silly thing slipped off your knee!
Pray don't apologize, old chap:
A very trivial mishap.
So clumsy of you? How absurd!
My dear Sir Smashum, not a word!
Now do sit down and have another,
And tell us all about your brother—
You know, the one who broke his head.
Is the poor fellow still in bed?
A chair—allow me, sir! . . . Great Scott!
That was a nasty smash! Eh, what?
Oh, not at all: the chair was old—
Queen Anne, or so we have been told.
We've got at least a dozen more
Just leave the pieces on the floor.
I want you to admire our view:
Come nearer to the window, do;
And look how beautiful . . . Tut, tut!
You didn't see that it was shut?
I hope you are not badly cut!
Not hurt? A fortunate escape!
Amazing! Not a single scrape!
And now, if you have finished tea,

I fancy you might like to see
A little thing or two I've got.
That china plate? Yes, worth a lot:
A beauty too . . . Ah, there it goes!
I trust it didn't hurt your toes?
Your elbow brushed it off the shelf?
Of course: I've done the same myself.
And now, my dear Sir Smashum—Oh,
You surely don't intend to go?
You must be off? Well, come again,
So glad you're fond of porcelain.

E. V. RIEU

Limericks

There was a young man from Bengal
Who went to a fancy dress ball;
He thought he would risk it
And go as a biscuit
But a dog ate him up in the hall.

'Open wide,' said a dentist called Bert
To a man-eating shark whose teeth hurt.
'When I've finished the drilling
I'll give you a filling.'
He did—and the filling was Bert.

There was an old man from Nantucket
Who kept all his cash in a bucket.
His daughter, named Nan,
Ran away with a man,
And as for the bucket, Nan tucket.

There was a young man of Japan
Who wrote verse that never would scan.
When they said, 'But the thing
Doesn't go with a swing,'
He said, 'Yes, but I always like to get as
  many words into the last line as I possibly can.'

Lim

There once was a bard from Hong Kong
Who thought limericks were too long.

GERARD BENSON

Combinations

A flea flew by a bee. The bee
To flee the flea flew by a fly.
The fly flew high to flee the bee
Who flew to flee the flea who flew
To flee the fly who now flew by.

The bee flew by the fly. The fly
To flee the bee flew by the flea.
The flea flew high to flee the fly
Who flew to flee the bee who flew
To flee the flea who now flew by.

The fly flew by the flea. The flea
To flee the fly flew by the bee.
The bee flew high to flee the flea
Who flew to flee the fly who flew
To flee the bee who now flew by.

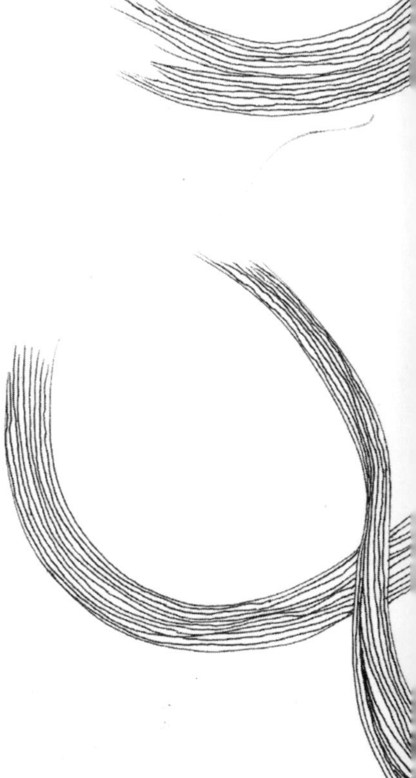

The flea flew by the fly. The fly
To flee the flea flew by the bee.
The bee flew high to flee the fly
Who flew to flee the flea who flew
To flee the bee who now flew by.

The fly flew by the bee. The bee
To flee the fly flew by the flea.
The flea flew high to flee the bee
Who flew to flee the fly who flew
To flee the flea who now flew by.

The bee flew by the flea. The flea
To flee the bee flew by the fly.
The fly flew high to flee the flea
Who flew to flee the bee who flew
To flee the fly who now flew by.

MARY ANN HOBERMAN

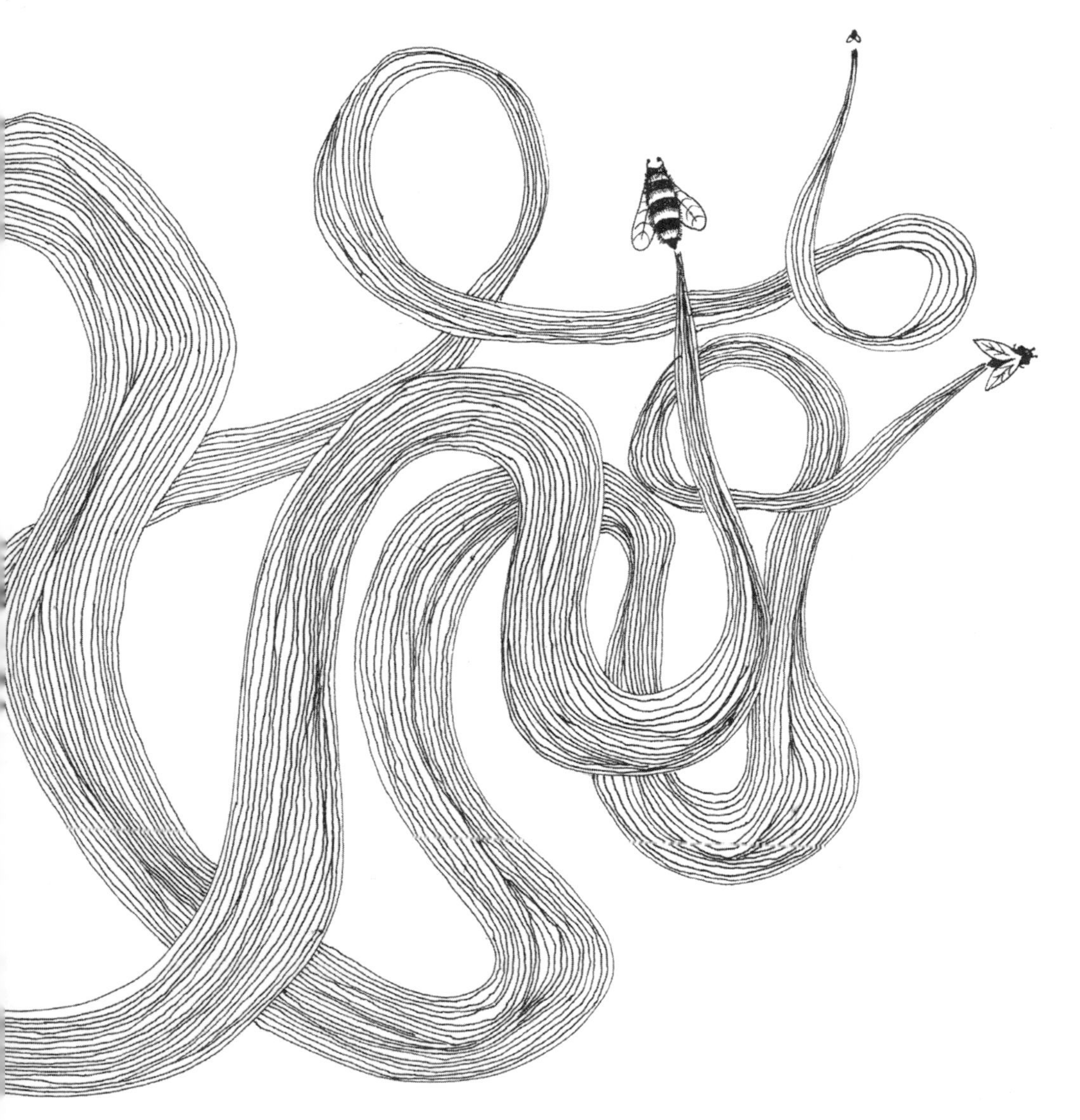

Who Knows?

I know
Something you don't know.

No, you don't,
I know it.

You don't know it.
How could you know it!
Nobody knows it,
Only me.

I just know it.

Prove it, then.
Tell me what I know.

Tell yourself.
Why should I tell you?
You're the one
Who knows it.
Yes, but you *don't* know it!
You prove it.

I can't prove it.
How can I prove it?
If I tell you what I know
You'll say you know it already.

I do know it already.

Well, *you* prove it.

No, I can't prove it.
If I tell you what I know
You know,
You'll change it to something else.

No, I won't.
If you tell me
What you know I know,
I'll know if you know it.

Yes, but I *won't* know!

That's all right.
Then I'll know
Something you don't know.

ALLAN AHLBERG

sametimedotcom
(A really useful website)

Learn how to clean out the hamster cage
And improve your language skills
At the same time!

Learn how to mend a bicycle puncture
And play the saxophone
At the same time!

Learn how to bake chocolate brownies
And strengthen your tennis serve
At the same time!

Learn how to tap dance
And study the movement of the planets
At the same time!

Learn how to rub your tummy in a circular motion
(with one hand)
And the top of your head (with the other)
At the same time!

ROGER MCGOUGH

The Uncertainty of the Poet

I am a poet.
I am very fond of bananas.

I am bananas.
I am very fond of a poet.

I am a poet of bananas.
I am very fond.

A fond poet of 'I am, I am'—
Very bananas.

Fond of 'Am I bananas?
Am I?'—a very poet.

Bananas of a poet!
Am I fond? Am I very?

Poet bananas! I am.
I am fond of a 'very'.

I am of very fond bananas.
Am I a poet?

WENDY COPE

Trying Places

There's more to Angmering than Avening
And Barking and Barling are fun,
So are Baulking and Bilting and Beeswing and Birling
Now see what I find I've begun.

I'd rather be Chittering than Cooling;
Of Detling and Didling I'm less sure;
But when Ealing and Epping and Feering and Felling
I really can't ask for much more.

Be careful if Gedling or Goring
And Havering and Hawling beware;
But Iping and Jeving(ton), Kemsing and Kettering
You can really enjoy while you're there.

It's fun to be Larling or Lunning
And Matching and Melling's OK
But Nursling and Newbigging, Oving and Oxspring
Depend very much on the day.

Be daring when Pickering or Postling
And Quadring and Rickling need friends;
While Skeffling and Stebbing and Tendring and Terling
Be sure you know where it all ends.

You ought to try Ulting or Venning
(ton); Wartling or Wichling instead;
Exning or Yalding—but now I've been Thaxted
And Buxted and Oxted and Haxted and Elsted
As I can't find an *ing* on a Z!

ANTHONY STUART

Jabberwocky

'Twas brillig, and the slithy toves
   Did gyre and gimble in the wabe;
All mimsy were the borogoves,
   And the mome raths outgrabe.

'Beware the Jabberwock, my son!
   The jaws that bite, the claws that catch!
Beware the Jubjub bird, and shun
   The frumious Bandersnatch!'

He took his vorpal sword in hand:
   Long time the manxome foe he sought—
So rested he by the Tumtum tree,
   And stood a while in thought.

And as in uffish thought he stood,
   The Jabberwock, with eyes of flame,
Came whiffling through the tulgey wood,
   And burbled as it came!

One, two! One two! And through and through
   The vorpal blade went snicker-snack!
He left it dead, and with its head
   He went galumphing back.

'And hast thou slain the Jabberwock?
   Come to my arms, my beamish boy!
O frabjous day! Callooh! Callay!'
   He chortled in his joy.

'Twas brillig, and the slithy toves
   Did gyre and gimble in the wabe;
All mimsy were the borogoves,
   And the mome raths outgrabe.

LEWIS CARROLL

Ruinous Rhymes

Pussycat, pussycat, where have you been,
Licking your lips with your whiskers so clean?
Pussycat, pussycat, purring and pudgy,
Pussycat, pussycat. WHERE IS OUR BUDGIE?

This little pig went to market
But I think that the point is well taken—
It's the cute little pig that wisely stayed home
Who succeeded in saving his bacon.

Mary, Mary, quite contrary,
How does your garden grow?
With snails and frogs and neighbours' dogs
And terribly, terribly slow.

Sing a song of sixpence?
It's hardly worth the sound.
So if you want my singing
Please offer me a pound.

When Old Mother Hubbard
Went to the cupboard
Her dog for a morsel would beg.
'Not a scrap can be found,'
She explained to her hound
So he bit the poor dear on the leg.

MAX FATCHEN

Father William

'You are old, Father William,' the young man said,
　'And your hair has become very white;
And yet you incessantly stand on your head—
　Do you think, at your age, it is right?'

'In my youth,' Father William replied to his son,
　'I feared it might injure the brain;
But, now that I'm perfectly sure I have none,
　Why, I do it again and again.'

'You are old,' said the youth, 'as I mentioned before,
　And have grown most uncommonly fat;
Yet you turned a back-somersault in at the door—
　Pray, what is the reason of that?'

'In my youth,' said the sage, as he shook his grey locks,
　'I kept all my limbs very supple
By the use of this ointment—one shilling the box—
　Allow me to sell you a couple?'

'You are old,' said the youth, 'and your jaws are too weak
　For anything tougher than suet;
Yet you finished the goose, with the bones and the beak—
　Pray, how did you manage to do it?'

'In my youth,' said his father, 'I took to the law,
And argued each case with my wife;
And the muscular strength, which it gave to my jaw,
Has lasted the rest of my life.'

'You are old,' said the youth, 'one would hardly suppose
That your eye was as steady as ever;
Yet you balanced an eel on the end of your nose—
What made you so awfully clever?'

'I have answered three questions, and that is enough,'
Said his father; 'don't give yourself airs!
Do you think I can listen all day to such stuff?
Be off, or I'll kick you down stairs!'

LEWIS CARROLL

Solomon Grundy

Solomon Grundy,
Born on Monday,
Christened on Tuesday,
Married on Wednesday,
Took ill on Thursday,
Worse on Friday,
Died on Saturday,
Buried on Sunday,
So that was the end
  of Solomon Grundy.

ANON.

Birthdays

Monday's child is fair of face,
Tuesday's child is full of grace,
Wednesday's child is full of woe,
Thursday's child has far to go,
Friday's child is loving and giving,
Saturday's child works hard for its living;
But the child who is born on the Sabbath day
Is bonny and blithe and good and gay.

ANON.

Sneezing

Sneeze on Monday, sneeze for danger;
Sneeze on Tuesday, miss a stranger;
Sneeze on Wednesday, get a letter;
Sneeze on Thursday, something better;
Sneeze on Friday, sneeze for sorrow;
Sneeze on Saturday, see your sweetheart tomorrow.

ANON.

Why Did the Chicken?

Starting out across the road
The clever little chicken slowed
Then stopped. *I'm blowed*
It clucked *if I can see*
Why they should make a joke of me
And turned back, very sensibly.

JOHN MOLE

My
Life

My Life

Look at it coming
down the street
toward us:
it chokes me up
every time I see it
walking along
all by itself.
How does it know
for example
which corner
is the right one
to turn at?
Who tells it
to keep going
past the intersection
and take the first left
after the supermarket?
There it goes—
I'll follow quietly
and see where
it's off to.

JULIE O'CALLAGHAN

poem for rodney

people always ask what
am i going to be
when i grow
up and i always
just think
i'd like to grow
up

NIKKI GIOVANNI

When I Was Three

When I was three I had a friend
Who asked me why bananas bend,
I told him why, but now I'm four,
I'm not so sure . . .

RICHARD EDWARDS

New Baby

My baby brother makes so much noise
that the Rottweiler next door
phoned up to complain.

My baby brother makes so much noise
that all the big green frogs
came out the drains.

My baby brother makes so much noise
that the rats and the mice
wore headphones.

My baby brother makes so much noise
that I can't ask my mum a question,
so much noise that sometimes

I think of sitting the cat on top of him
in his pretty little cot with all his teddies.
But even the cat is terrified of his cries.

So I have devised a plan. A soundproof room.
A telephone to talk to my mum.
A small lift to receive food and toys.

Thing is, it will cost a fortune.
The other thing is, the frogs have gone.
It's not bad now. Not that I like him or anything.

JACKIE KAY

The Babysitter

It was clear
From the moment
They walked out the door
That Tracey
Had never done
This job before.

Until they came home
She patiently sat
On me
        my little brother
                                and the cat.

LINDSAY MACRAE

My Love For You

I know you little, I love you lots;
My love for you would fill ten pots,
Fifteen buckets, sixteen cans,
Three teacups and four dishpans.

TRADITIONAL

Happiness

John had
Great Big
Waterproof
Boots on;
John had a
Great Big
Waterproof
Hat;
John had a
Great Big
Waterproof
Mackintosh—
And that
(Said John)
Is
That.

A. A. MILNE

You Were the Mother Last Time

'You were the mother last time.
It's my turn today.'
        'It's *my* turn.'
'No, *my* turn.'
        'All right then, I won't play.'
'Oh, go ahead then, *be* the mother.
It's not fair.
But I don't care.'

'I was the father last time.
I won't be today.'
        'It's your turn.'
'No, *your* turn.'
        'All right then, I won't play.'
'Oh, never mind, *don't* be the father.
It's not fair.
But I don't care.'

'I was the sister last time.
It's your turn today.'
        'It is not.'
'It is so.'
        'All right then, I won't play.'
'Oh, never mind, *don't* be the sister.
It's not fair.
But I don't care.'

'I have an idea!
Let's *both* be mothers!
(We'll pretend
About the others.)'

MARY ANN HOBERMAN

The Quarrel

I quarrelled with my brother
I don't know what about,
One thing led to another
And somehow we fell out.
The start of it was slight,
The end of it was strong,
He said he was right,
I knew he was wrong!

We hated one another.
The afternoon turned black.
Then suddenly my brother
Thumped me on the back,
And said, 'Oh, *come* along!
We can't go on all night—
I was in the wrong.'
So he was in the right.

ELEANOR FARJEON

Me

My Mum is on a diet,
My Dad is on the booze,
My Gran's out playing Bingo
And she was born to lose.

My brother's stripped his motorbike
Although it's bound to rain.
My sister's playing Elton John
Over and over again.

What a dim old family!
What a dreary lot!
Sometimes I think that I'm the only
Superstar they've got.

KIT WRIGHT

Fame

The best thing
about being famous

is when you walk
down the street

and people turn round
to look at you

and bump into things.

ROGER MCGOUGH

Middle Child

The piggy in the middle
The land between sky and sea
The cheese which fills the sandwich
The odd one out of three
The one who gets the hand-me-downs
And broken bits of junk
The follower, not the leader
The one in the bottom bunk

The one for whom the pressure's off
The one who can run wild
The one who holds the balance of power
The lucky second child

LINDSAY MACRAE

Chicken Poxed

My sister was spotty,
Real spotty all over,
She was plastered with spots
From her head to her toes.

She had spots on the parts
That her bathing suits cover,
Spots on her eyelids,
Spots on her nose.

I didn't know chickenpox
Could be so interesting,
It seemed such a shame
To waste all those spots.

So when Jody was sleeping
And no one was looking,
I got a blue pen
And connected her dots.

VALERIE BLOOM

Children Imagining a Hospital
for Kingswood County Primary School

I would like kindness, assurance,
A wide selection of books;
Lots of visitors, and a friend
To come and see me:
A bed by the window so I could look at
All the trees and fields, where I could go for a walk.
I'd like a hospital with popcorn to eat.
A place where I have my own way.

I would like HTV all to myself
And people bringing tea round on trollies;
Plenty of presents and plenty of cards
(I would like presents of food).
Things on the walls, like pictures, and things
That hang from the ceiling;
Long corridors to whizz down in wheelchairs.
Not to be left alone.

U. A. FANTHORPE

Teabag

I'd like to be a teabag,
and stay at home all day
and talk to other teabags
in a teabag sort of way.

I'd love to be a teabag,
and lie in a little box
and never have to wash my face
or change my dirty socks.

I'd like to be a Tetley bag,
an Earl Grey one perhaps,
and doze all day and lie around
with Earl Grey kind of chaps.

I wouldn't have to do a thing,
no homework, jobs or chores—
just lie inside a comfy box
of teabags and their snores.

I wouldn't have to do exams,
I needn't tidy rooms,
or sweep the floor, or feed the cat
or wash up all the spoons.

I wouldn't have to do a thing—
A life of bliss, you see . . .
except that once in all my life

I'd make a cup of tea.

PETER DIXON

The Vegetables Strike Back

I don't like vegetables at all,
said Nathan one evening at tea.
But what the young lad didn't know,
was that vegetables hear and see.

I don't like you as it happens,
said a voice from out of the mash.
I was a fine young potato,
till you had me boiled and smashed.

Just think how you would like to be skinned,
or baked alive in your jacket.
How would you feel to be crumpled up,
and stuffed inside of a packet.

You tear peas out of their houses,
and drag them away from their mums.
You stick knives into baby beans,
and forks into cucumbers' bums.

You fatten a lettuce or cabbage,
and cut off its head with a knife.
Drive runner beans up bamboo poles,
in order to choke them of life.

I have good friends who've been frozen,
or left in a shed to shrink up.
Some were burned up in an oven,
and some became soup in a cup.

You spread fear in every garden,
when you come to kill and destroy.
Stabbing, cutting and slicing,
with your latest gardening toy.

You say you don't like vegetables,
well we don't like vandals like you,
Who pack us into bags and boxes,
then drown us in steaming hot stew.

The mouth of the boy fell open,
his fork hovered high in the air.
His knife was all ready to cut,
did he dare? did he dare?

STEVE TURNER

Tomato Ketchup

If you do not shake the bottle
None'll come and then a lot'll.

ANON.

Yellow Butter

Yellow butter purple jelly red jam black bread

Spread it thick
Say it quick

Yellow butter purple jelly red jam black bread

Spread it thicker
Say it quicker

Yellow butter purple jelly red jam black bread

Now repeat it
While you eat it

Yellow butter purple jelly red jam black bread

Don't talk
With your mouth full!

MARY ANN HOBERMAN

Kids

'Sit up straight,'
Said mum to Mabel.
'Keep your elbows
Off the table.
Do not eat peas
Off a fork.
Your mouth is full—
Don't try and talk.
Keep your mouth shut
When you eat.
Keep still or you'll
Fall off your seat.
If you want more,
You will say "please".
Don't fiddle with
That piece of cheese!'
If then we kids
Cause such a fuss,
Why do you go on
Having us?

SPIKE MILLIGAN

The Story of Fidgety Philip

Let me see if Philip can
Be a little gentleman;
Let me see, if he is able
To sit still for once at table:
Thus Papa bade Phil behave;
And Mamma look'd very grave.
But fidgety Phil,
He won't sit still;
He wriggles
And giggles,
And then, I declare,
Swings backwards and forwards
And tilts up his chair,
Just like any rocking horse;—
'Philip! I am getting cross!'

See the naughty restless child
Growing still more rude and wild,
Till his chair falls over quite.
Philip screams with all his might.
Catches at the cloth, but then
That makes matters worse again.
Down upon the ground they fall.
Glasses, plates, knives, forks and all.
How Mamma did fret and frown.
When she saw them tumbling down!
And Papa made such a face!
Philip is in sad disgrace.

Where is Philip, where is he?
Fairly cover'd up you see!
Cloth and all are lying on him;
He has pull'd down all upon him.
What a terrible to-do!
Dishes, glasses, snapt in two!
Here a knife, and there a fork!
Philip, this is cruel work.
Table all so bare, and ah!
Poor Papa, and poor Mamma
Look quite cross, and wonder how
They shall make their dinner now.

HEINRICH HOFFMAN

I'm Just Going Out

I'm just going out for a moment.

Why?

To make a cup of tea.

Why?

Because I'm thirsty.

Why?

Because it's hot.

Why?

Because the sun's shining.

Why?

Because it's summer.

Why?

Because that's when it is.

Why?

Why don't you stop saying why?

Why?

Tea-time why.
High-time-you-stopped-saying-why-time.

What?

MICHAEL ROSEN

Rabbiting On

Where did you go?
Oh . . . nowhere much.

What did you see?
Oh . . . rabbits and such.

Rabbits? What else?
Oh . . . a rabbit hutch.

What sort of rabbits?
What sort? Oh . . . small.

What sort of hutch?
Just a hutch, that's all.

But what did it look like?
Like a rabbit hutch.

Well, what was in it?
Small rabbits and such.

I worried about you
While you were gone.

Why don't you stop
Rabbiting on?

KIT WRIGHT

How Can I?

How can I wind up my brother
when I haven't got the key?

How can I turn on my charm
when I can't even find the switch?

How can I snap at my mother
when I'm not a crocodile?

How can I stir up my sister
when I'm not even holding a spoon?

How can I pick up my feet
and not fall to the ground on my knees?

How can I stretch my legs
when they're long enough already?

Parents!—They ask the impossible!

BRIAN MOSES

Dear Mum

Dear Mum,
While you were out
A cup went and broke itself on purpose.
A crack appeared in that tatty blue vase
Your great Grandad got from Mr Ming in China.
Somehow without me even turning on the tap
The sink mysteriously overflowed
And a strange jam-stain,
About the size of a boy's hand,
Suddenly appeared on the kitchen wall.
Mum, I don't think we will ever discover
Exactly how the cat
Managed to turn on the washing machine—
Specially from the inside,
Or how sis's pet rabbit
Went and mistook
The waste-disposal unit for a burrow.
Also Mum,
I know the canary looks grubby,
But it took me ages getting it out of the vacuum cleaner.
I was being good, honest,
But I think the house is haunted so,
Knowing you're going to have a fit,
I've gone over to Gran's to lie low for a bit.

BRIAN PATTEN

Father Says

Father says
Never
let
me
see
you
doing
that
again
father says
tell you once
tell you a thousand times
come hell or high water
his finger drills my shoulder
never let me see you doing that again

My brother knows all his phrases off by heart
so we practise them in bed at night.

MICHAEL ROSEN

Just Fancy That

'Just fancy that!' my parents say
At anything I mention.
They always seem so far away
And never pay attention.

'Just fancy that,' their eyes are glazed.
It grows so very wearing.
'Just fancy that' is not a line
For which I'm really caring.

And so today I'm telling them
I threw a cricket bat.
I broke a windowpane at school.
They murmur, 'Fancy that.'

I wrote a message on the fence.
I spoke a wicked word.
The way the vicar hurried past,
I'm positive he heard.

'Just fancy that.' Then suddenly
Their eyes are sticking out,
Their words are coming in a rush
Their voices in a shout.

'You naughty child, you shameless boy,
It's time WE had a chat.'
Hurrah, they've noticed me at last.
My goodness, fancy that!

MAX FATCHEN

Matilda

Who Told Lies, and Was Burned to Death

Matilda told such Dreadful Lies,
It made one Gasp and Stretch one's Eyes;
Her Aunt, who, from her Earliest Youth,
Had kept a Strict Regard for Truth,
Attempted to Believe Matilda:
The effort very nearly killed her,
And would have done so, had not She
Discovered this Infirmity.
For once, towards the Close of Day,
Matilda, growing tired of play,
And finding she was left alone,
Went tiptoe to the Telephone
And summoned the Immediate Aid
Of London's Noble Fire-Brigade.
Within an hour the Gallant Band
Were pouring in on every hand,
From Putney, Hackney Downs, and Bow
With Courage high and Hearts a-glow
They galloped, roaring through the Town,
'Matilda's House is Burning Down!'
Inspired by British Cheers and Loud
Proceeding from the Frenzied Crowd,
They ran their ladders through a score
Of windows on the Ball Room Floor;

And took Peculiar Pains to Souse
The Pictures up and down the House,
Until Matilda's Aunt succeeded
In showing them they were not needed;
And even then she had to pay
To get the Men to go away!

It happened that a few Weeks later
Her Aunt was off to the Theatre
To see that Interesting Play
The Second Mrs Tanqueray.
She had refused to take her Niece
To hear this Entertaining Piece:
A Deprivation Just and Wise
To Punish her for Telling Lies.
That Night a Fire *did* break out—
You should have heard Matilda Shout!
You should have heard her Scream and Bawl,
And throw the window up and call
To People passing in the Street—
(The rapidly increasing Heat
Encouraging her to obtain
Their confidence)—but all in vain!
For every time She shouted 'Fire!'
They only answered 'Little Liar!'
And therefore when her Aunt returned,
Matilda, and the House, were Burned.

HILAIRE BELLOC

On Turning Ten

The whole idea of it makes me feel
like I'm coming down with something,
something worse than any stomach ache
or the headaches I get from reading in bad light—
a kind of measles of the spirit,
a mumps of the psyche,
a disfiguring chicken pox of the soul.

You tell me it is too early to be looking back,
but that is because you have forgotten
the perfect simplicity of being one
and the beautiful complexity introduced by two.
But I can lie on my bed and remember every digit.
At four I was an Arabian wizard.
I could make myself invisible
by drinking a glass of milk in a certain way.
At seven I was a soldier, at nine a prince.

But now I am mostly at the window
watching the late afternoon light.
Back then it never fell so solemnly
against the side of my tree house,
and my bicycle never leaned against the garage
as it does today,
all the dark blue speed drained out of it.

This is the beginning of sadness, I say to myself,
as I walk through the universe in my sneakers.
It is time to say goodbye to my imaginary friends,
time to turn the first big number.

It seems only yesterday I used to believe
there was nothing under my skin but light.
If you cut me I would shine.
But now when I fall upon the sidewalks of life,
I skin my knees. I bleed.

BILLY COLLINS

Supermarket

I'm
lost
among a
maze of cans
behind a pyramid
of jams, quite near
asparagus and rice,
close to the Oriental spice,
and just before sardines.

I hear my mother calling, 'Joe.
Where are you, Joe?
Where did you
Go?' And I reply in a voice concealed
among the candied orange peel,
and packs of Chocolate Dreams.

'I
hear
you, Mother
dear, I'm here—
quite near the ginger ale
and beer, and lost among a
maze
of cans
behind a
pyramid of jams
quite near asparagus
and rice, close to the
Oriental spice, and just
before sardines.'

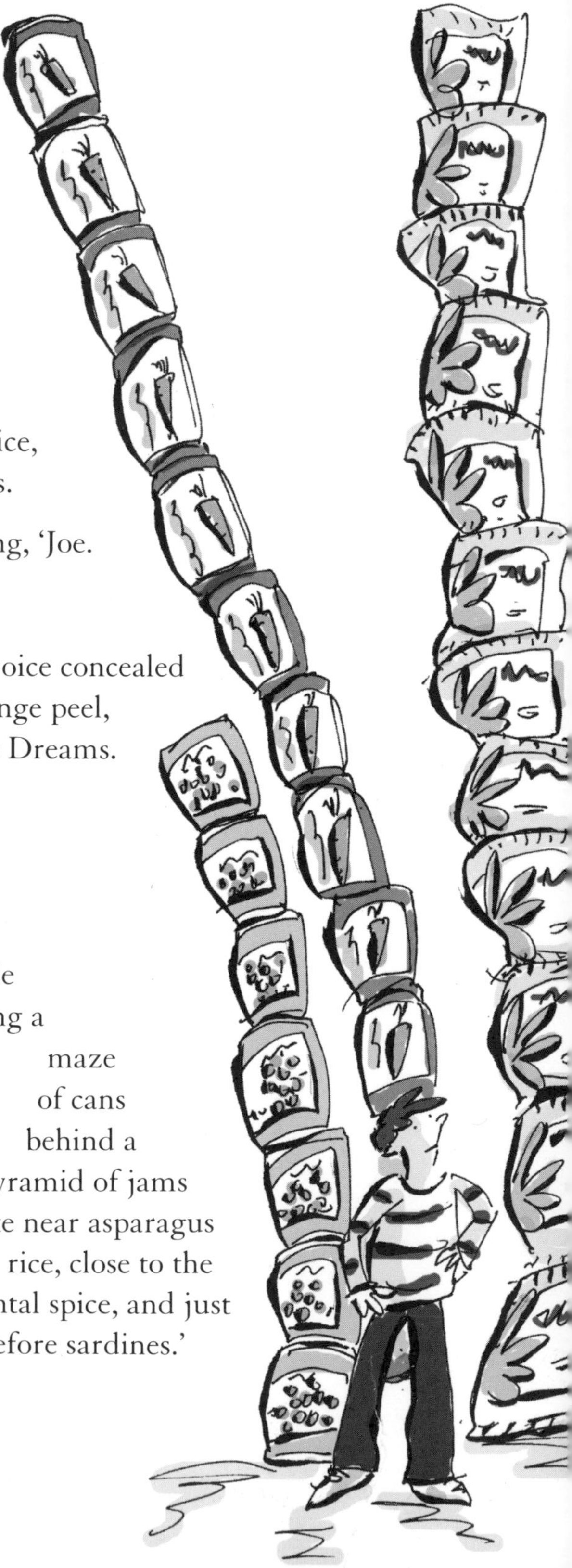

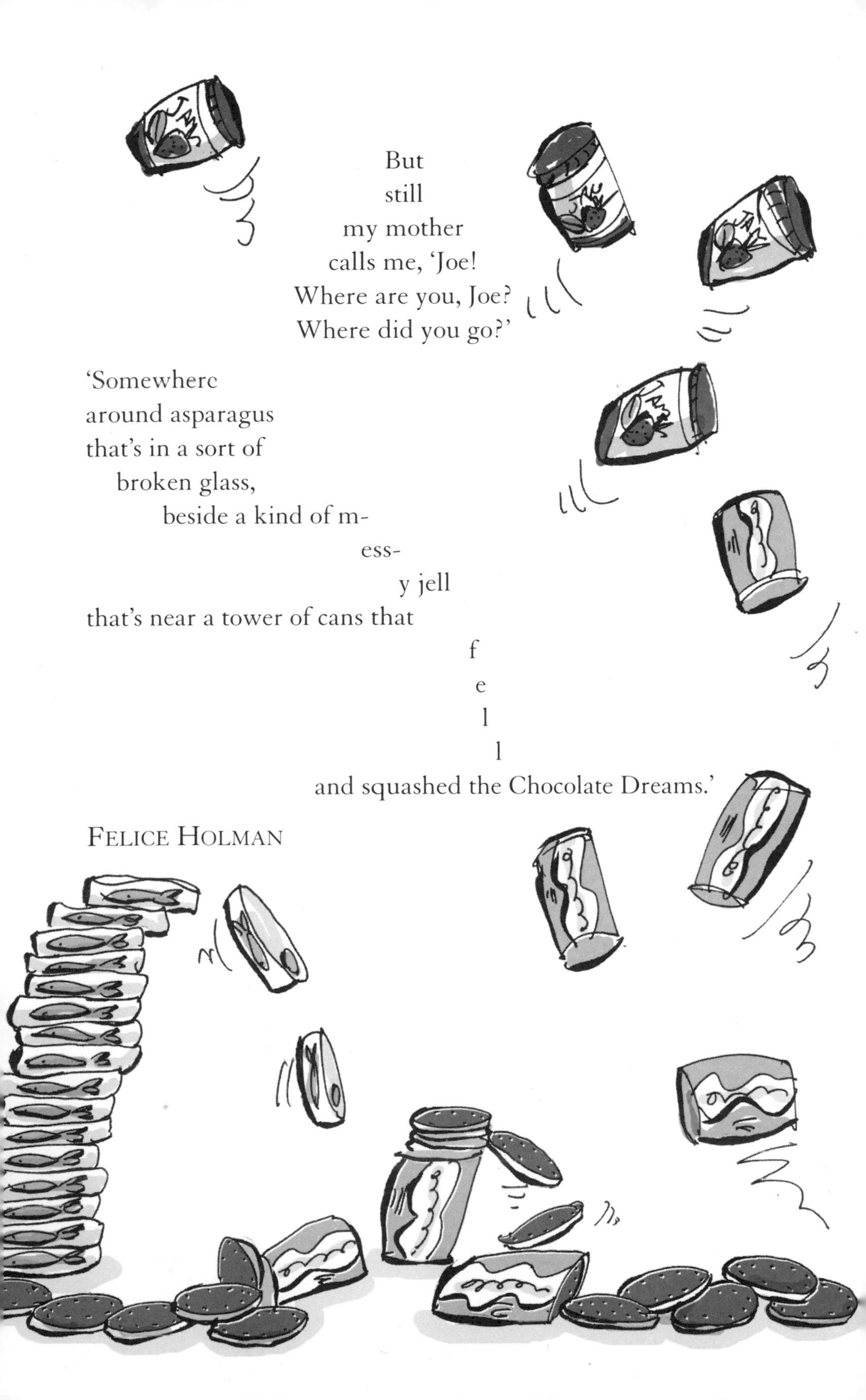

But
still
my mother
calls me, 'Joe!
Where are you, Joe?
Where did you go?'

'Somewhere
around asparagus
that's in a sort of
broken glass,
beside a kind of m-
ess-
y jell
that's near a tower of cans that
f
e
l
l
and squashed the Chocolate Dreams.'

FELICE HOLMAN

No Bread

I wish I'd made a list,
I forgot to get the bread.
If I forget it again
I'll be dead.

We had blank and butter pudding,
Beans on zip.
Boiled egg with deserters,
No chip butty: just chip.

I wish I'd made a list,
I forgot to get the bread.
My mam got the empty bread bin
And wrapped it round my head.

Our jam sarnies were just jam
Floating on the air.
We spread butter on the table
'cos the bread wasn't there.

My mam says if I run away
She knows I won't be missed,
Not like the bread was . . .
I wish I'd made a list!

IAN MCMILLAN

Greedyguts

I sat in the café and sipped at a Coke.
There sat down beside me a WHOPPING great bloke
Who sighed as he elbowed me into the wall:
'Your trouble, my boy, is your belly's too small!
Your bottom's too thin! Take a lesson from me:
I may not be nice, but I'm GREAT, you'll agree,
And I've lasted a lifetime by playing this hunch:
The bigger the breakfast, the larger the lunch!

The larger the lunch, then the huger the supper.
The deeper the teapot, the vaster the cupper.
The fatter the sausage, the fuller the tea.
The MORE on the table, the BETTER FOR ME!'

His elbows moved in and his elbows moved out,
His belly grew bigger, chins wobbled about,
As forkful by forkful and plate after plate,
He ate and he ate and he ate and he ATE!

I hardly could breathe, I squashed out of shape,
So under the table I made my escape.

'Aha!' he rejoiced, 'when it's put to the test,
The fellow who's fattest will come off the best!
Remember, my boy, when it comes to the crunch:
The bigger the breakfast, the larger the lunch!

The larger the lunch, then the huger the supper.
The deeper the teapot, the vaster the cupper.
The fatter the sausage, the fuller the tea.
The MORE on the table, the BETTER FOR ME!'

A lady came by who was scrubbing the floor
With a mop and a bucket. To even the score,
I lifted that bucket of water and said,
As I poured the whole lot of it over his head:

'*I've* found all my life, it's a pretty sure bet:
The FULLER the bucket, the WETTER YOU GET!'

KIT WRIGHT

The Magic Handbag

When Granny comes to stay
She brings her black handbag.
As soon as she's in through the door,
'Let me see what I've got here,'
She says.
She opens her bag
And in goes her hand
And out come my favourite sweets.

If I need a pencil to draw the cat,
If she needs scissors to cut my nails,
If I scrape my knee and need a plaster,
'Let me see what I've got here,'
She says.
She opens her bag
And in goes her hand
And out comes whatever I need.

At home her bag behaves itself
And nothing strange is ever let out.
But once Granny and I are off on a walk
Just anything can come out of that bag.

One hot afternoon we are in the park.
'I'm tired and I'm hot,' I say.
'Let me see what I've got here,'
She says.
She opens her bag
And in goes her hand
And out comes a cone of strawberry ice-cream.

Suddenly we hear a noise, a humming brown noise.
'Bees,' says Granny, 'a swarm of bees.
Let me see what I've got here,'
She says.
She opens her bag
But she doesn't put in her hand
She holds it open and, with a noise
Like the bath emptying,
All the bees swarm in.
'There,' says Granny, and shuts her bag,
'Let's go home for a cup of tea.'

It was a long way home. 'What we need,'
I say, 'is a short cut.'
'Let me see what I've got here,'
She says.
She opens her bag
And puts it down on the pavement.
She takes hold of my hand, and then,
And then we are in a huge dark cave.
There's a slight buzzing sound
And a smell of honey. 'Come on!'
Says Granny. 'We'll be late for tea.'

We step out into the sunlight
And there we are outside home,
And in we go, in time for tea.
'Let me see what I've got here,'
She says.
She opens her bag
And in goes her hand
And out comes a jar of honey.

MICHAEL RICHARDS

My Grandpa

The truth of the matter, the truth of the matter—
As one who supplies us with hats is a Hatter,
As one who is known for his growls is a Growler—
My Grandpa traps owls, yes, my Grandpa's an Owler.

Though owls, alas, are quite out of fashion,
Grandpa keeps busy about his profession
And hoards every owl that falls to his traps:
'Someday,' says he, 'they'll be needed, perhaps.'

'Owls are such sages,' he says, 'I surmise
Listening to owls could make the world wise.'
Nightlong his house is shaken with hoots,
And he wakes to owls in his socks and his boots.

Owls, owls, nothing but owls,
The most fantastical of fowls:
White owls from the Arctic, black owls from the Tropic.
Some are far-sighted, others myopic.

There are owls on his picture frames, owls on his chairs,
Owls in dozens ranked on his stairs.
Eyes, eyes, rows of their eyes.
Some are big as collie dogs, some are thumb-size.

Deep into Africa, high into Tibet
He travels with his rubber mouse and wiry owl-net:
The rarest of owls, and the very most suspicious
Will pounce on the mouse and be tangled in the meshes.

'Whatever you could wish to know, an owl will surely
  know it,'
My Grandpa says proudly. 'And how does he show it?
Sleeping and thinking and sleeping and thinking—
Letting a horrible hoot out and winking!'

TED HUGHES

Just My Luck

'If weasels could fly,' said my Granny,
'I would give you four buckets of sweets,
Three mousetraps, two spoons and a tom-tom,
And lots more magnificent treats.'

'Then give me them now, quick!' I shouted
As a furry thing whizzed past my throat,
But she shook her head answering 'Sorry,
I said weasels, dear, that was a stoat.'

RICHARD EDWARDS

'Granny Smith: Best Before Feb 21'
(Notice seen in Sainsbury's)

I can't remember
when I was best before
but I do now wonder
what Granny Smith
will suddenly do
on February twenty-two:
dance naked down
Sainsbury's aisles,
trolley-slalom
staid shoppers
shouting out
ancient hymns?
I'm glad she's not
my own granny.
Mine was always, always
best before bedtime.

JOHN CORBEN

High Life

My home is on the eighty-ninth floor.
I live above the storms.

My windows are the cockpit
of an airplane that never flies.

The builders thought they were smart
but the wind is smarter

and I grow dizzy and weak
as I watch the water in my sink

flop back and forth
as we blow to and fro.

I grab the towel rack
to steady myself.

A wispy cloud
crashes through my livingroom wall.

I scream over the phone
'What's the weather like down there?'

JULIE O'CALLAGHAN

Chairs

Chairs
Seem
To
Sit
Down
On
Themselves, almost as if
They were people,
Some fat, some thin;
Settled comfortably
On their own seats,
Some even stretch out their arms
To
Rest.

VALERIE WORTH

The Spare Room

It was just the spare room
the nobody-there room
the spooks-in-the-air room
the unbearable spare room.

It wasn't the guest room
the four-poster best room
the designed-to-impress room
the unusable guest room.

It wasn't the main room
the homely and plain room
the flop-on-the-bed room
Mum and Dad's own room.

It wasn't the blue room
the sweet lulla-loo room
the creep-on-your-feet room
the baby's asleep room.

It wasn't the bright room
the clothes-everywhere room
the music-all-night room
sister's scattered-about room.

It was just the spare room
the nobody-there room
the spooks-in-the-air room
the unbearable spare room.

DIANA HENDRY

Off to School
7+8=15

Schoolitis

You haven't got a cough,
You haven't got mumps,
You haven't got a chill
Or any funny lumps.
You haven't got tummy-ache,
You haven't got a fever,
You haven't got a runny nose
Or chicken-pox either.
You don't look a ruin,
You don't look a wreck,
You haven't got toothache
Or a pain in the neck.
You're as fit as a fiddle,
You're sound as a bell,
In fact I've never ever
Seen you looking so well!
You don't fool me,
I'm no fool.
Now up out of bed
AND OFF TO SCHOOL!

BRIAN PATTEN

First Day at School

A millionbillionwillion miles from home
Waiting for the bell to go. (To go where?)
Why are they all so big, other children?
So noisy? So much at home they
must have been born in uniform
Lived all their lives in playgrounds
Spent the years inventing games
that don't let me in. Games
that are rough, that swallow you up.

And the railings.
All around, the railings.
Are they to keep out wolves and monsters?
Things that carry off and eat children?
Things you don't take sweets from?
Perhaps they're to stop us getting out
Running away from the lessins. Lessin.
What does a lessin look like?
Sounds small and slimy.
They keep them in glassrooms.
Whole rooms made out of glass. Imagine.

I wish I could remember my name
Mummy said it would come in useful.
Like wellies. When there's puddles.
Yellowwellies. I wish she was here.
I think my name is sewn on somewhere
Perhaps the teacher will read it for me.
Tea-cher. The one who makes the tea.

ROGER MCGOUGH

Sally

She was a dog-rose kind of girl:
elusive, scattery as petals;
scratchy sometimes, tripping you like briars.
She teased the boys
turning this way and that, not to be tamed
or taught any more than the wind.
Even in school the word 'ought'
had no meaning for Sally.
On dull days
she'd sit quiet as a mole at her desk
delving in thought.
But when the sun called
she was gone, running the blue day down
till the warm hedgerows prickled the dusk
and the moths flickered out.

Her mother scolded; Dad
gave her the hazel-switch,
said her head was stuffed with feathers
and a starling tongue.
But they couldn't take the shine out of her.
Even when it rained
you felt the sun saved under her skin.
She'd a way of escape
laughing at you from the bright end of a tunnel,
leaving you in the dark.

PHOEBE HESKETH

Playgrounds

Playgrounds are such gobby places.
Know what I mean?
Everyone seems to have something to
Talk about, giggle, whisper, scream and shout about.
I mean, it's like being in a parrot cage.

And playgrounds are such pushy places.
Know what I mean?
Everyone seems to have to
Run about, jump, kick, do cartwheels, handstands, fly
around.
I mean, it's like being inside a whirlwind.

And playgrounds are such patchy places.
Know what I mean?
Everyone seems to
Go round in circles, lines and triangles, coloured shapes.
I mean, it's like being in a kaleidoscope.

And playgrounds are such pally places.
Know what I mean?
Everyone seems to
Have best friends, secrets, link arms, be in gangs.
Everyone, except me.

Know what I mean?

BERLIE DOHERTY

Best Friends

It's Susan I talk to not Tracey,
Before that I sat next to Jane;
I used to be best friends with Lynda
But these days I think she's a pain.

Natasha's all right in small doses,
I meet Mandy sometimes in town;
I'm jealous of Annabel's pony
And I don't like Nicola's frown.

I used to go skating with Catherine,
Before that I went there with Ruth;
And Kate's so much better at trampoline:
She's a showoff, to tell you the truth.

I think that I'm going off Susan,
She borrowed my comb yesterday;
I *think* I might sit next to Tracey,
She's my nearly best friend: she's OK.

ADRIAN HENRI

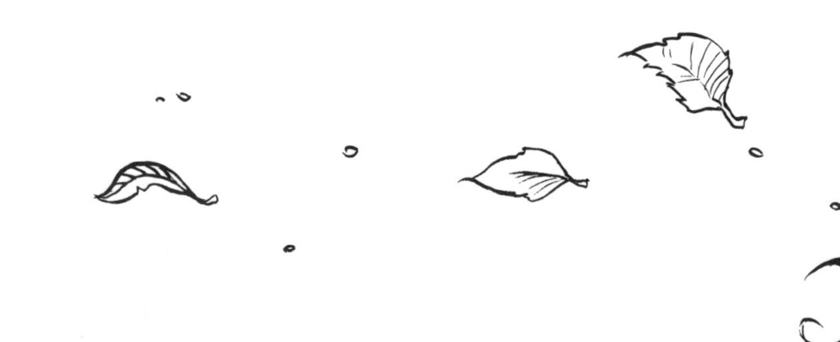

Friends

I fear it's very wrong of me,
And yet I must admit,
When someone offers friendship
I want the *whole* of it.
I don't want everybody else
To share my friends with me.
At least, I want *one* special one,
Who, indisputably

Likes me much more than all the rest,
Who's always on my side,
Who never cares what others say,
Who lets me come and hide
Within his shadow, in his house—
It doesn't matter where—
Who lets me simply be myself,
Who's always, *always* there.

ELIZABETH JENNINGS

Tich Miller

Tich Miller wore glasses
with elastoplast-pink frames
and had one foot three sizes larger than the other.

When they picked teams for outdoor games
she and I were always the last two
left standing by the wire-mesh fence.

We avoided one another's eyes,
stooping, perhaps, to re-tie a shoelace,
or affecting interest in the flight

of some fortunate bird, and pretended
not to hear the urgent conference:
'Have Tubby!' 'No, no, have Tich!'

Usually they chose me, the lesser dud,
and she lolloped, unselected,
to the back of the other team.

At eleven we went to different schools.
In time I learned to get my own back,
sneering at hockey-players who couldn't spell.

Tich died when she was twelve.

WENDY COPE

I Asked the Little Boy

I asked the little boy who cannot see,
'And what is colour like?'
'Why, green,' said he,
'Is like the rustle when the wind blows through
The forest; running water, that is blue;
And red is like a trumpet sound; and pink
Is like the smell of roses; and I think
That purple must be like a thunderstorm;
And yellow is like something soft and warm;
And white is a pleasant stillness when you lie
And dream.'

ANON.

Nativity Play

This year . . .
This year can I be Herod?
This year, can I be him?
A wise man
or a Joseph?
An inn man
or a king?

This year . . .
can I be famous?
This year, can I be best?
Bear a crown of silver
and wear a golden vest?

This year . . .
can I be starlight?
This year, can I stand out?
. . . feel the swish of curtains
and hear the front row shout
'Hurrah' for good old Ronny
he brings a gift of gold
head afire with tinsel
'The Greatest Story Told . . .'
'Hurrah for good old Herod!'
and shepherds from afar.

So—
don't make me a palm tree
And can I be—
a Star?

PETER DIXON

Being in a Bad Mood

. . . is a bit like being
stuck in a soggy anorak
with no arms, no zip
and a huge wet flapping hood
which sits on your head
like a tired-out seagull.
You know you've got
to pull yourself out of it
or else suffer
when the sun appears.

LINDSAY MACRAE

Don't Care

Don't care was made to care,
Don't care was hung;
Don't care was put in the pot
And boiled till he was done.

TRADITIONAL

A Poison Tree

I was angry with my friend:
I told my wrath, my wrath did end.
I was angry with my foe:
I told it not, my wrath did grow.

And I watered it in fears,
Night and morning with my tears;
And I sunned it with smiles,
And with soft deceitful wiles.

And it grew both day and night,
Till it bore an apple bright;
And my foe beheld it shine,
And he knew that it was mine,

And into my garden stole
When the night had veiled the pole:
In the morning glad I see
My foe outstretched beneath the tree.

WILLIAM BLAKE

Jack

That's Jack;
Lay a stick on his back!
What's he done? I cannot say.
We'll find out tomorrow,
And beat him today.

CHARLES HENRY ROSS

The Bully Asleep

One afternoon, when grassy
Scents through the classroom crept,
Bill Craddock laid his head
Down on his desk, and slept.

The children came round him:
Jimmy, Roger, and Jane;
They lifted his head timidly
And let it sink again.

'Look, he's gone sound asleep, Miss,'
Said Jimmy Adair;
'He stays up all the night, you see;
His mother doesn't care.'

'Stand away from him, children.'
Miss Andrews stooped to see.
'Yes, he's asleep; go on
With your writing, and let him be.'

'Now's a good chance!' whispered Jimmy;
And he snatched Bill's pen and hid it.
'Kick him under the desk, hard;
He won't know who did it.'

'Fill all his pockets with rubbish—
Paper, apple-cores, chalk.'
So they plotted, while Jane
Sat wide-eyed at their talk.

Not caring, not hearing,
Bill Craddock he slept on;
Lips parted, eyes closed—
Their cruelty gone.

'Stick him with pins!' muttered Roger.
'Ink down his neck!' said Jim.
But Jane, tearful and foolish,
Wanted to comfort him.

JOHN WALSH

Dreaming Black Boy

I wish my teacher's eyes wouldn't
go past me today. Wish he'd know
it's okay to hug me when I kick
a goal. Wish I myself wouldn't
hold back when an answer comes.
I'm no woodchopper now
like all ancestors.

I wish I could be educated
to the best of tune up, and earn
good money and not sink to lick
boots. I wish I could go on every
crisscross way of the globe
and no persons or powers or
hotel keepers would make it a waste.

I wish life wouldn't spend me out
opposing. Wish same way creation
would have me stand it would have
me stretch, and hold high, my voice
Paul Robeson's, my inside eye
a sun. Nobody wants to say
hello to nasty answers.

I wish torch throwers of night
would burn lights for decent times.
Wish plotters in pyjamas would pray
for themselves. Wish people wouldn't
talk as if I dropped from Mars.

I wish only boys were scared
behind bravados, for I could suffer
I could suffer a big big lot.
I wish nobody would want to earn
the terrible burden I can suffer.

JAMES BERRY

Truth

Sticks and stones may break my bones,
but words can also hurt me.
Stones and sticks break only skin,
while words are ghosts that haunt me.

Slant and curved the word-swords fall
to pierce and stick inside me.
Bats and bricks may ache through bones,
but words can mortify me.

Pain from words has left its scar
on mind and heart that's tender.
Cuts and bruises now have healed;
it's words that I remember.

BARRIE WADE

Names

Today my best pal, *my number one*,
called me a *dirty darkie,*
when I wouldn't give her a sweetie.
I said, softly, 'I would never believe
you of all people, Char Hardy,
would say that word to me.
Others, yes, the ones
that are stupid and ignorant,
and don't know better, but
not you, Char Hardy, not you.
I thought I could trust you.
I thought you were different.
But I must have been mistaken.'

Char went a very strange colour.
Said a most peculiar, 'Sorry,'
as if she was swallowing her voice.
Grabbed me, hugged me, begged me
to forgive her. She was crying.
I didn't mean it. I didn't mean it.
I felt the playground sink. *Sorry. Sorry.*
A see-saw rocked, crazy, all by itself.
An orange swing swung high on its own.
My voice was hard as a steel frame:
'Well then, what exactly did you mean?'

JACKIE KAY

Four O'Clock Friday

Four o'clock Friday, I'm home at last,
Time to forget the week that's past.
On Monday, in break they stole my ball
And threw it over the playground wall.
On Tuesday afternoon, in games
They threw mud at me and called me names.
On Wednesday, they trampled my books on the floor,
So Miss kept me in because I swore.
On Thursday, they laughed after the test
'Cause my marks were lower than the rest.
Four o'clock Friday, at last I'm free,
For two whole days they can't get at me.

JOHN FOSTER

Absent Player

Ball games her agony,
at rounders she was posted out
and placed at the furthest
possible position
under a tree almost.

Lost, as usual, dreaming,
she heard some vague panic noises
breaking through, as if, desperate,
the whole team were shouting
'Catch the ball! Catch the ball! Catch it!'

She slowly turned her face upwards.
She did not see the ball,
but it aimed at a resistance
and came down straight, smack
onto a well-shaped mouth.

Her front teeth were loosened
in blood. She lay on the grass.
No way could she tell any
sympathy from boiling rage
around her. She cried, quietly.

JAMES BERRY

The Footballer's Love of the Ball

Grab the ball and boot it high
See it going up the sky
See it falling down and then
Boot it straight back up again.

Boot it high and boot it higher
Boot it almost out of sight
Send it shooting up at teatime
See it tumbling back at night.

See it rise and see it fall
Earth to sky and ball to ball.

ALLAN AHLBERG

Polite Children

May we have our ball, please
May we have it back?
We never meant to lose it
Or give it such a whack.

It shot right past the goalie
It shot right past the goal
And really then what happened next
Was out of our control.

It truly was such rotten luck
For all concerned that you
Were halfway up a ladder
When the ball came flying through.

We also very much regret
What happened to your cat
It's tragic when an animal
Gets landed on like that.

Your poor wife too we understand
Was pretty much upset
When phoning for the doctor
And phoning for the vet.

She quite forgot the oven.
It simply is no joke
When your husband's half unconscious
And your house is full of smoke.

The fire-brigade, of course, meant well
It wasn't their mistake
That there was no fire to speak of
Just a bit of well-done steak.

Still clouds have silver linings
And pains are soon forgot
While your lawn will surely flourish
From the hosing that it got.

The game of life is never lost
The future's not all black
And the ball itself seems quite unmarked.
So . . . may we have it back?

ALLAN AHLBERG

The Park

In the middle of the city
Is an open space called a Park;
It is difficult for us to do what we like there
Even after dark.

In the middle of the Park there is a statue,
A huge man made of stone;
We are not allowed to climb his legs or scribble on his
    trousers,
He has to be left alone.

In the middle of the grass there is some water
Surrounded by an asphalt path;
We are forbidden to fish or throw stones into it
Or swim or take a bath.

In the middle of the water is an island
Full of mysterious things,
But none of us has ever set foot upon it
Because none of us has wings.

Olive Dehn

Running and Catching

There was a girl
And she could run as fast as anything
Faster than a racing bike.
She could leap and jump over the crags with mountain
animals
But she couldn't catch a ball.

And there was a boy:
Long arms shot out, he could catch anything
Small balls on a bounce
Frisbees that whizz past your nose like speeded-up planets
But he couldn't run at all.

High in the air, low on the ground, he caught.
She leapt over fences and ran great distances.
He couldn't run for toffee, not even for a bus.
She couldn't catch, even if you gently threw her a baby's
ball.

So when the time came for the summer fair, and there
were games in the field
What should they do? They teamed up, it was obvious.
The fleet-footed, elastic-armed, catching-and-running pair
Won all the prizes, and by the next year's fair
The girl could catch balls and the boy never missed a bus.

JENNY JOSEPH

California Skateboard Park, 1977

The guys are there,
I must be good,
As they can see.
I take a breath
And push my board
Accelerate
The curving stone
Till suddenly
I reach the top,
I kick to turn
To spark my trucks
And raise a cheer
For grinding gear.

No time to fear,
I crouch and pump
The swooping bowl
That swallows speed.
My knees are bent
To grip the deck
And leave this earth
To fly through air,
A weightless boy
Who's earned his wings
And every clap;
I smoothly land
And slide to stop
Now out of breath
The guys go yeah!
I hear them sing
I **am** the king.

ANDREW FUSEK PETERS

Playing a Dazzler

You bash drums playing a dazzler;
I worry a trumpet swaying with it.

You dance, you make a girl's skirt swirl;
I dance, I dance by myself.

You bowl, I lash air and my wicket;
I bowl, you wallop boundary balls.

Your goal-kick beat me between my knees;
my goal-kick flies into a pram-and-baby.

You eat off your whole-pound chocolate cake;
I swell up halfway to get my mate's help.

My bike hurls me into the hedge;
your bike swerves half-circle from trouble.

I jump the wall and get dumped;
you leap over the wall and laugh, satisfied.

I touch the country bridge and walk;
you talk and talk.

You write poems with line-end rhymes;
I write poems with rhymes nowhere or anywhere.

Your computer game screens monsters and gunners;
my game brings on swimmers and courting red birds.

JAMES BERRY

There Was an Orchestra

There was an orchestra—Bingo-Bango
Playing for us to dance the tango
And the people all clapped as we arose
For her sweet face and my new clothes.

F. SCOTT FITZGERALD

Holidays at Home

There was a family who, every year,
Would go abroad, sometimes to Italy,
Sometimes to France. The youngest did not dare
To say, 'I much prefer to stay right here.'

You see, abroad there were no slot-machines,
No bright pink rock with one name going through it,
No rain, no boarding-houses, no baked beans,
No landladies, and no familiar scenes.

And George, the youngest boy, so longed to say,
'I don't like Greece, I don't like all those views,
I don't like having fierce sun every day,
And, most of all, I just detest the way

The food is cooked—that garlic and that soup,
Those strings of pasta, and no cakes at all.'
The family wondered why George seemed to droop
And looked just like a thin hen in a coop.

They never guessed why when they said, 'Next year
We can't afford abroad, we'll stay right here,'
George looked so pleased and soon began to dream
Of piers, pink rock, deep sand, and Devonshire cream.

ELIZABETH JENNINGS

There Isn't Time!

There Isn't Time!

There isn't time, there isn't time
To do the things I want to do,
With all the mountain-tops to climb,
And all the woods to wander through,
And all the seas to sail upon,
And everywhere there is to go,
And all the people, every one
Who lives upon the earth to know.
There's only time, there's only time
To know a few, and do a few,
And then sit down and make a rhyme
About the rest I want to do.

ELEANOR FARJEON

The Moment

To write down all I contain at this moment
I would pour the desert through an hour-glass,
The sea through a water-clock,
Grain by grain and drop by drop
Let in thc trackless, measureless, mutable seas and sands.

For earth's days and nights are breaking over me
The tides and sands are running through me,
And I have only two hands and a heart to hold
    the desert and the sea.

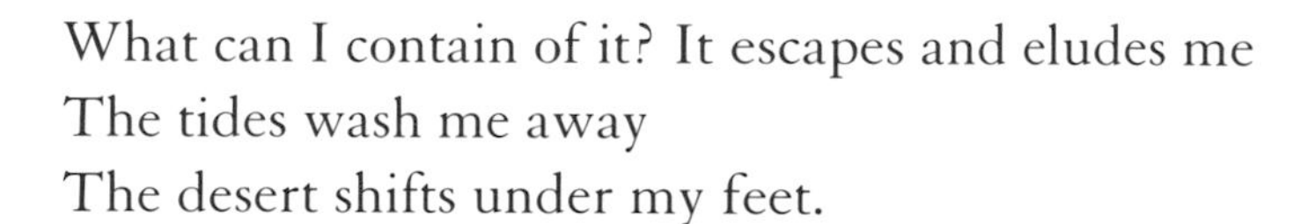

What can I contain of it? It escapes and eludes me
The tides wash me away
The desert shifts under my feet.

KATHLEEN RAINE

I Stepped from Plank to Plank

I stepped from plank to plank,
A slow and cautious way;
The stars about my head I felt,
About my feet the sea.

I knew not but the next
Would be my final inch.
This gave me that precarious gait
Some call experience.

EMILY DICKINSON

Half-Past Two

Once upon a schooltime
He did Something Very Wrong
(I forget what it was).

And She said he'd done
Something Very Wrong, and must
Stay in the school-room till half-past two.

(Being cross, she'd forgotten
She hadn't taught him Time.
He was too scared at being wicked to remind her.)

He knew a lot of time: he knew
Gettinguptime, timeyouwereofftime,
Timetogohomenowtime, TVtime,

Timeformykisstime (that was Grantime).
All the important times he knew,
But not half-past two.

He knew the clockface, the little eyes
And two long legs for walking,
But he couldn't click its language,

So he waited, beyond onceupona,
Out of reach of all the timefors,
And knew he'd escaped for ever

Into the smell of old chrysanthemums on Her desk,
Into the silent noise his hangnail made,
Into the air outside the window, into ever.

And then, *My goodness*, she said,
Scuttling in, *I forgot all about you.*
Run along or you'll be late.

So she slotted him back into schooltime,
And he got home in time for teatime,
Nexttime, notimeforthatnowtime,

But he never forgot how once by not knowing time,
He escaped into the lockless land of ever,
Where time hides tick-less waiting to be born.

U. A. FANTHORPE

Leisure

What is this life if, full of care,
We have no time to stand and stare?

No time to stand beneath the boughs
And stare as long as sheep or cows.

No time to see, when woods we pass,
Where squirrels hide their nuts in grass.

No time to see, in broad daylight,
Streams full of stars, like skies at night.

No time to turn at beauty's glance,
And watch her feet, how they can dance.

No time to wait till her mouth can
Enrich that smile her eyes began.

A poor life this if, full of care,
We have no time to stand and stare.

W. H. DAVIES

The Road Not Taken

Two roads diverged in a yellow wood,
And sorry I could not travel both
And be one traveller, long I stood
And looked down one as far as I could
To where it bent in the undergrowth;

Then took the other, as just as fair,
And having perhaps the better claim,
Because it was grassy and wanted wear;
Though as for that the passing there
Had worn them really about the same,

And both that morning equally lay
In leaves no step had trodden black.
Oh, I kept the first for another day!
Yet knowing how way leads on to way,
I doubted if I should ever come back.

I shall be telling this with a sigh
Somewhere ages and ages hence:
Two roads diverged in a wood, and I—
I took the one less travelled by;
And that has made all the difference.

ROBERT FROST

Bed in Summer

In winter I get up at night
And dress by yellow candle-light.
In summer, quite the other way,
I have to go to bed by day.

I have to go to bed and see
The birds still hopping on the tree,
Or hear the grown-up people's feet
Still going past me in the street.

And does it not seem hard to you,
When all the sky is clear and blue,
And I should like so much to play,
To have to go to bed by day?

ROBERT LOUIS STEVENSON

The Star

Twinkle, twinkle, little star,
How I wonder what you are!
Up above the world so high,
Like a diamond in the sky.

When thc blazing sun is gone,
When he nothing shines upon,
Then you show your little light,
Twinkle, twinkle, all the night.

Then the traveller in the dark,
Thanks you for your tiny spark,
He could not see which way to go,
If you did not twinkle so.

In the dark blue sky you keep,
And often through my curtains peep,
For you never shut your eye,
Till the sun is in the sky.

As your bright and tiny spark,
Lights the traveller in the dark—
Though I know not what you are,
Twinkle, twinkle, little star.

JANE TAYLOR

Why Is It?

Why is it that the taps all drip,
The electricity wires trip,
Tired pipes in the attic grumble,
Empty washer-dryers tumble,
Floorboards creak and old joints moan,
Doorposts squeak and rafters groan,
Fridges softly hum and sigh,
Cats out in the garden cry
Like a band of mad banshees,
The wind howls eerily in the trees,
The telephone rings, there's no one there,
There are soft whispers in the air,
The moon starts playing hide and seek,
Your head feels light, your knees feel weak,
You think you're not alone in bed,
And wish you were elsewhere instead,

When you're alone at night?

VALERIE BLOOM

The Night Mail

This is the night mail crossing the border,
Bringing the cheque and the postal order,
Letters for the rich, letters for the poor,
The shop at the corner and the girl next door,
Pulling up Beattock, a steady climb—
The gradient's against her but she's on time.

Past cotton grass and moorland boulder,
Shovelling white steam over her shoulder,
Snorting noisily as she passes
Silent miles of wind-bent grasses;
Birds turn their heads as she approaches,
Stare from the bushes at her blank-faced coaches;
Sheepdogs cannot turn her course,
They slumber on with paws across;
In the farm she passes no one wakes
But a jug in a bedroom gently shakes.

Dawn freshens, the climb is done.
Down towards Glasgow she descends
Towards the steam tugs, yelping down the glade
 of cranes
Towards the fields of apparatus, the furnaces
Set on the dark plain like gigantic chessmen.
All Scotland waits for her;
In the dark glens, beside the pale-green sea lochs,
Men long for news.

Letters of thanks, letters from banks,
Letters of joy from the girl and boy,
Receipted bills and invitations

To inspect new stock or visit relations,
And applications for situations.
And timid lovers' declarations,
And gossip, gossip from all the nations,
News circumstantial, news financial,
Letters with holiday snaps to enlarge in,
Letters with faces scrawled on the margin.
Letters from uncles, cousins and aunts,

Letters to Scotland from the South of France,
Letters of condolence to Highlands and Lowlands,
Notes from overseas to the Hebrides;
Written on paper of every hue,
The pink, the violet, the white and the blue,
The chatty, the catty, the boring, adoring,
The cold and official and the heart's outpouring,
Clever, stupid, short and long,
The typed and the printed and the spelt all wrong.

Thousands are still asleep
Dreaming of terrifying monsters
Or a friendly tea beside the band at Cranston's or
  Crawford's;
Asleep in working Glasgow, asleep in well-set Edinburgh,
Asleep in granite Aberdeen.
They continue their dreams
But shall wake soon and long for letters.
And none will hear the postman's knock
Without a quickening of the heart,
For who can bear to feel himself forgotten?

W. H. AUDEN

Reindeer Report

Chimneys: colder.
Flightpaths: busier.
Driver: Christmas (F)
Still baffled by postcodes.

Children: more.
And stay up later.
Presents: heavier.
Pay: frozen.

Mission in spite
Of all this
Accomplished.

U. A. FANTHORPE

Secrets

High on the branch of a tree,
a bird in its nest chirped:
I grasp what I grasp.
A secret's a worm that hides
in the earth, slides about in the gloom,
sifting the whispering soil
where flowers unwrap.

Down by the bright green pond,
a frog on its lily croaked:
I ken what I ken.
A secret's a dragonfly key
locking, unlocking, the air
where silvery fish jump high
for the hooks of the fishermen.

Out in the shimmering meadow,
a bee in a flower buzzed:
I suss what I suss.
Blown on a breeze,
a secret's a dusting of pollen
carried downwind in the sunlight
to end in a sneeze.

Snug in her bed in her room,
a child in her blankets crooned:
I know what I know.
A secret's a shadow thrown on a wall,
all fingers and thumbs,
which dances, dances for me
till the darkness comes.

CAROL ANN DUFFY

A Tent

A tent went up on the grass:
just room for a boy and his brother,
who waited for day to pass—
kept wishing that day would pass
as they'd never wished of another.

At last they got their wish.
Darkness fell and off they went
feeling quite daredevilish—
yes, really daredevilish—
to spend a night in that tent.

Night is dizzy and deep;
the wall of a tent is thin;
they were almost too scared to sleep,
but whispered each other to sleep
as stars and ghosts listened in.

And the tent flew through the night
on the back of the turning world,
which brought them home all right,
them and the tent, still upright
and now lavishly dew-pearled.

CHRISTOPHER REID

Good Company

I sleep in a room at the top of the house
With a flea, and a fly, and a soft-scratching mouse,
And a spider that hangs by a thread from the ceiling,
Who gives me each day such a curious feeling
When I watch him at work on the beautiful weave
Of his web that's so fine I can hardly believe
It won't all end up in such terrible tangles,
For he sways as he weaves, and spins as he dangles.
I cannot get up to that spider, I know,
And I hope he won't get down to me here below,
And yet when I wake in the chill morning air
I'd miss him if he were not still swinging there,
For I have in my room such good company,
There's him, and the mouse, and the fly, and the flea.

LEONARD CLARK

Nightening

When you wake up at night
And it's dark and frightening,
Climb out of bed
And turn on the lightening.

MICHAEL DUGAN

Keep a Poem in Your Pocket

Keep a poem in your pocket
and a picture in your head
and you'll never feel lonely
at night when you're in bed.

The little poem will sing to you
the little picture bring to you
a dozen dreams to dance to you
at night when you're in bed.

So—
Keep a picture in your pocket
and a poem in your head
and you'll never feel lonely
at night when you're in bed.

Beatrice Schenk de Regniers

Night Lights

There is no need to light a nightlight
On a light night like tonight;
For a nightlight's light's a slight light
When the moonlight's white and bright.

Anon.

Small Dawn Song

This is just to say Thank You

to the tick
  of the downstairs clock
    like a blind man's stick
      tap-tip on through the dark

to the lone
  silly blackbird who sang
    before dawn when no one
      should have been listening

to the wheeze
  and chink of the milk float
    like an old nightwatchman clinking keys
      and clearing his throat

          Six o'clock and all's well
          Six o'clock and all's well

The night's been going on
                    so long
                    so long

This is just to say Thank You.

PHILIP GROSS

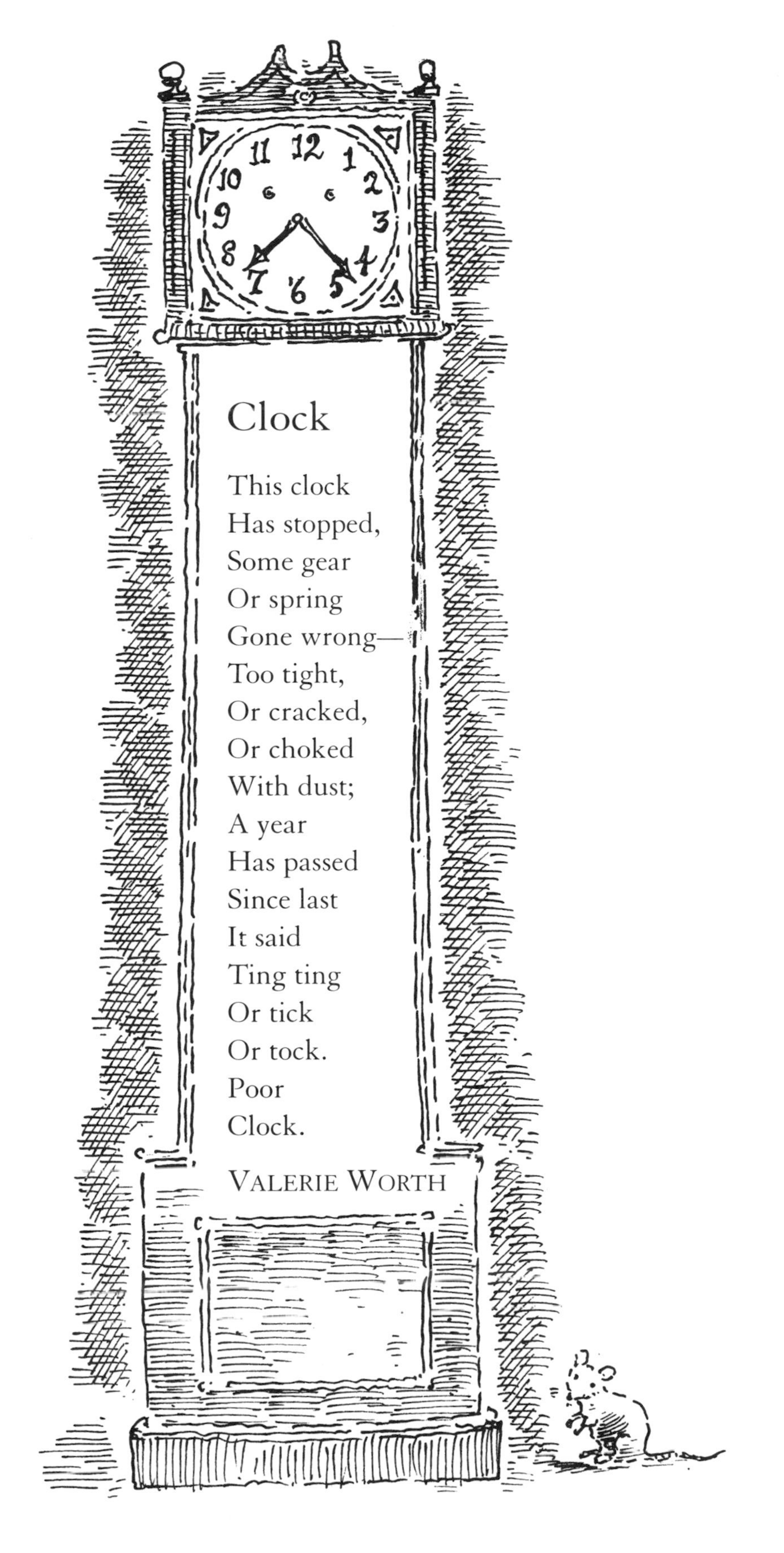

Clock

This clock
Has stopped,
Some gear
Or spring
Gone wrong—
Too tight,
Or cracked,
Or choked
With dust;
A year
Has passed
Since last
It said
Ting ting
Or tick
Or tock.
Poor
Clock.

VALERIE WORTH

Looking Forward

The days are getting longer.
From my first-floor window
I can sit and watch
the tide of people ebb and flow.
I know them all
the early-morning milkman
postman
paperboy
the schoolchild
worker
shopper.
I invent their lives.
Now I have started looking forward
to the sights and sounds
of summer evenings
by my open window
children playing late
lawnmowers
couples walking dogs.
And yet
perhaps this summer I shall not be here.
My days are getting shorter.

SUE COWLING

Song

When I am dead, my dearest,
  Sing no sad songs for me;
Plant thou no roses at my head,
  Nor shady cypress tree:
Be the green grass above me
  With showers and dewdrops wet;
And if thou wilt, remember,
  And if thou wilt, forget.
I shall not see the shadows,
  I shall not feel the rain;
I shall not hear the nightingale
  Sing on, as if in pain:
And dreaming through the twilight
  That doth not rise nor set,
Haply I may remember,
  And haply may forget.

CHRISTINA ROSSETTI

Unhappy Whispers

I whispered a lot
in my father's final weeks.
Some days are so terrible
you can't speak
in a normal tone about them.

You lose your voice
when sad things happen
and whispering fills
your mouth with words
you cannot bear to hear.

JULIE O'CALLAGHAN

Do Not Be Afraid

Do not stand at my grave and weep
I am not there, I do not sleep.
I am a thousand winds that blow,
I am the diamond glint on snow.
I am the sunlight on ripened grain,
I am the gentle autumn rain.
When you wake in the morning hush
I am the swift, uplifting rush
of quiet birds in circling flight.
I am the soft starlight at night.
Do not stand at my grave and weep
I am not there—I do not sleep.

ANON.

Ozymandias

I met a traveller from an antique land
Who said: Two vast and trunkless legs of stone
Stand in the desert . . . Near them, on the sand,
Half sunk, a shattered visage lies, whose frown,
And wrinkled lip, and sneer of cold command,
Tell that its sculptor well those passions read
Which yet survive, stamped on these lifeless things,
The hand that mocked them, and the heart that fed:
And on the pedestal these words appear:
'My name is Ozymandias, king of kings:
Look on my works, ye Mighty, and despair!'
Nothing beside remains. Round the decay
Of that colossal wreck, boundless and bare
The lone and level sands stretch far away.

PERCY BYSSHE SHELLEY

Here Dead Lie We

Here dead lie we because we did not choose
To live and shame the land from which we sprung.
Life, to be sure, is nothing much to lose;
But young men think it is, and we were young.

A. E. Housman

Abbey Tomb

I told them not to ring the bells
The night the Vikings came
Out of the sea and passed us by.
The fog was thick as cream
And in the abbey we stood still
As if our breath might blare
Or pulses rattle if we once
Stopped staring at the door.

Through the walls and through the fog
We heard them passing by.
The deafer monks thanked God too soon
And later only I
Could catch the sound of prowling men
Still present in the hills
So everybody else agreed
To ring the abbey bells.

And even while the final clang
Still snored upon the air,
And while the ringers joked their way
Down round the spiral stair,
Before the spit of fervent prayer
Had dried into the stone
The raiders came back through the fog
And killed us one by one.

Father Abbot at the altar
Lay back with his knees
Doubled under him, caught napping
In the act of praise.
Brother John lay unresponsive
In the warming room.
The spiders came out for the heat
And then the rats for him.

Under the level of the sheep
Who graze here all the time
We lie now, under tourists' feet
Who in good weather come.
I told them not to ring the bells
But centuries of rain
And blustering have made their tombs
Look just as right as mine.

PATRICIA BEER

Said the General

Said the General of the Army,
'I think that war is barmy'
So he threw away his gun:
Now he's having much more fun.

SPIKE MILLIGAN

By St Thomas Water

By St Thomas Water
Where the river is thin
We looked for a jam-jar
To catch the quick fish in.
Through St Thomas Church-yard
Jessie and I ran
The day we took the jam-pot
Off the dead man.

On the scuffed tombstone
The grey flowers fell,
Cracked was the water,
Silent the shell.
The snake for an emblem
Swirled on the slab,
Across the beach of sky the sun
Crawled like a crab.

'If we walk,' said Jessie,
'Seven times round,
We shall hear a dead man
Speaking underground.'
Round the stone we danced, we sang,
Watched the sun drop,
Laid our heads and listened
At the tomb-top.

Soft as the thunder
At the storm's start
I heard a voice as clear as blood,
Strong as the heart.
But what words were spoken
I can never say,
I shut my fingers round my head,
Drove them away.

'What are those letters, Jessie,
Cut so sharp and trim
All round this holy stone
With earth up to the brim?'
Jessie traced the letters
Black as coffin-lead.
'*He is not dead but sleeping,*'
Slowly she said.

I looked at Jessie,
Jessie looked at me,
And our eyes in wonder
Grew wide as the sea.
Past the green and bending stones
We fled hand in hand,
Silent through the tongues of grass
To the river strand.

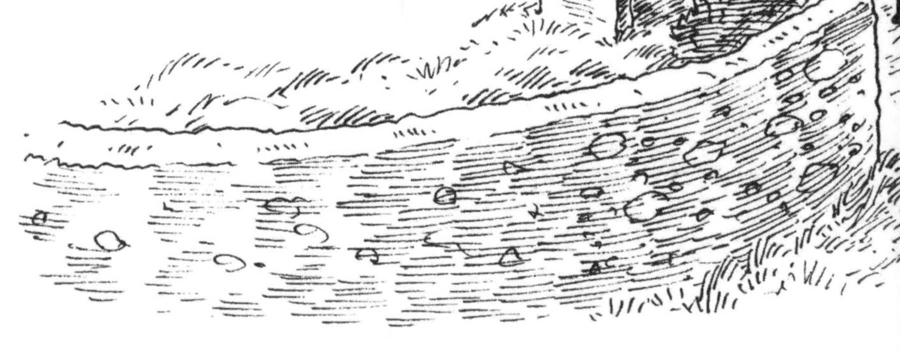

By the creaking cypress
We moved as soft as smoke
For fear all the people
Underneath awoke.
Over all the sleepers
We darted light as snow
In case they opened up their eyes,
Called us from below.

Many a day has faltered
Into many a year
Since the dead awoke and spoke
And we would not hear.
Waiting in the cold grass
Under a crinkled bough,
Quiet stone, cautious stone,
What do you tell me now?

CHARLES CAUSLEY

Uphill

Does the road wind uphill all the way?
  Yes, to the very end.
Will the day's journey take the whole long day?
  From morn to night, my friend.

But is there for the night a resting-place?
  A roof for when the slow, dark hours begin.
May not the darkness hide it from my face?
  You cannot miss that inn.

Shall I meet other wayfarers at night?
  Those who have gone before.
Then must I knock, or call when just in sight?
  They will not keep you waiting at that door.

Shall I find comfort, travel-sore and weak?
  Of labour you shall find the sum.
Will there be beds for me and all who seek?
  Yea, beds for all who come.

CHRISTINA ROSSETTI

If
I Were
Lord of
Tartary

Tartary

If I were Lord of Tartary,
   Myself and me alone,
My bed should be of ivory,
   Of beaten gold my throne;
And in my court should peacocks flaunt,
And in my forests tigers haunt,
And in my pools great fishes slant
   Their fins athwart the sun.

If I were Lord of Tartary,
   Trumpeters every day
To every meal would summon me,
   And in my courtyard bray;
And in the evening lamps would shine,
Yellow as honey, red as wine,
While harp, and flute, and mandoline,
   Made music sweet and gay.

If I were Lord of Tartary,
   I'd wear a robe of beads,
White, and gold, and green they'd be—
   And clustered thick as seeds;
And ere should wane the morning-star,
I'd don my robe and scimitar,
And zebras seven should draw my car
   Through Tartary's dark glades.

Lord of the fruits of Tartary,
   Her rivers silver-pale!
Lord of the hills of Tartary,
   Glen, thicket, wood, and dale!
Her flashing stars, her scented breeze,
Her trembling lakes, like foamless seas,
Her bird-delighting citron-trees
   In every purple vale!

Walter de la Mare

Fern Hill

Now as I was young and easy under the apple boughs
About the lilting house and happy as the grass was green,
    The night above the dingle starry,
        Time let me hail and climb
    Golden in the heydays of his eyes,
And honoured among the wagons I was prince of the
    apple towns
And once below a time I lordly had the trees and leaves
        Trail with daisies and barley
    Down the rivers of the windfall light.

And as I was green and carefree, famous among the barns
About the happy yard and singing as the farm was home,
    In the sun that is young once only,
        Time let me play and be
    Golden in the mercy of his means,
And green and golden I was huntsman and herdsman,
    the calves
Sang to my horn, the foxes on the hills barked clear and cold,
        And the sabbath rang slowly
    In the pebbles of the holy streams.

All the sun long it was running, it was lovely, the hay
Fields as high as the house, the tunes from the chimneys, it was air
    And playing, lovely and watery
        And fire green as grass.
    And nightly under the simple stars
As I rode to sleep the owls were bearing the farm away,
All the moon long I heard, blessed among stables, the nightjars
    Flying with the ricks, and horses
        Flashing into the dark.

And then to awake, and the farm, like a wanderer white
With the dew, come back, the cock on his shoulder: it was all
    Shining, it was Adam and maiden,
        The sky gathered again
    And the sun grew round that very day.
So it must have been after the birth of the simple light
In the first, spinning place, the spellbound horses walking warm
    Out of the whinnying green stable
        On to the fields of praise.

And honoured among foxes and pheasants by the gay house
Under the new made clouds and happy as the heart was long,
    In the sun born over and over,
        I ran my heedless ways,
    My wishes raced through the house high hay
And nothing I cared, at my sky blue trades, that
    time allows
In all his tuneful turning so few and such morning songs
    Before the children green and golden
        Follow him out of grace,

Nothing I cared, in the lamb white days, that time would
    take me
Up to the swallow thronged loft by the shadow of my hand,
    In the moon that is always rising,
        Nor that riding to sleep
    I should hear him fly with the high fields
And wake to the farm forever fled from the childless land.
Oh as I was young and easy in the mercy of his means,
        Time held me green and dying
    Though I sang in my chains like the sea.

DYLAN THOMAS

Reflections

I know a town
That's upside down
Beside a lake
(Still waters make
This town I know
To seem like so).

And standing here
If down I peer,
I see someone
Who finds it fun
To always do
As I do too.

And if I throw
A stone, although
I soon can make
Her small world shake,
She comes back when
It's calm again.

Likewise this town
That's upside down:
Afloat upon
The lake, a swan
Can briefly make
Its buildings shake.

COLIN WEST

Lines and Squares

Whenever I walk in a London street,
I'm ever so careful to watch my feet;
    And I keep in the squares,
    And the masses of bears,
Who wait at the corners all ready to eat
The sillies who tread on the lines of the street,
    Go back to their lairs,
    And I say to them, 'Bears,
Just look how I'm walking in all the squares!'

And the little bears growl to each other, 'He's mine,
As soon as he's silly and steps on a line.'
And some of the bigger bears try to pretend
That they came round the corner to look for a friend;
And they try to pretend that nobody cares
Whether you walk on the lines or squares.
But only the sillies believe their talk;
It's ever so portant how you walk.
And it's ever so jolly to call out, 'Bears,
Just watch me walking in all the squares!'

A. A. MILNE

Stone in the Water

Stone in the water,
Stone on the sand,
Whom shall I marry
When I get to land?

Will he be handsome
Or will he be plain,
Strong as the sun
Or rich as the rain?

Will he be dark
Or will he be fair,
And what will be the colour
That shines in his hair?

Will he come late
Or will he come soon,
At morning or midnight
Or afternoon?

What will he say
Or what will he sing,
And will he be holding
A plain gold ring?

Stone in the water
Still and small,
Tell me if he comes,
Or comes not at all.

CHARLES CAUSLEY

To Any Reader

As from the house your mother sees
You playing round the garden trees,
So you may see, if you will look
Through the windows of this book,
Another child, far, far away,
And in another garden, play.
But do not think you can at all,
By knocking on the window, call
That child to hear you. He intent
Is all on his play-business bent.
He does not hear; he will not look,
Nor yet be lured out of his book.
For, long ago, the truth to say,
He has grown up and gone away,
And it is but a child of air
That lingers in the garden there.

ROBERT LOUIS STEVENSON

The Way Through the Woods

They shut the road through the woods
  Seventy years ago.
Weather and rain have undone it again,
  And now you would never know
There was once a road through the woods
  Before they planted the trees.

It is underneath the coppice and heath,
  And the thin anemones.
  Only the keeper sees
That, where the ring-dove broods,
  And the badgers roll at ease,
There was once a road through the woods.

Yet, if you enter the woods
  Of a summer evening late,
When the night-air cools on the trout-ringed pools
  Where the otter whistles his mate,
(They fear not men in the woods,
  Because they see so few)
You will hear the beat of a horse's feet
  And the swish of a skirt in the dew,
  Steadily cantering through
The misty solitudes,
  As though they perfectly knew
The old lost road through the woods . . .
But there is no road through the woods.

RUDYARD KIPLING

Ghost in the Garden

The ghost in the garden
Cracks twigs as she treads
Shuffles the leaves
But isn't there

The ghost in the garden
Snaps back the brambles
So they spring against my legs
But isn't there

Draws spiders' webs across my face
Breathes mist on my cheek
Whispers with bird-breath down my ear
But isn't there

Tosses raindrops down from branches
Splashes the pond
Traces a face in it
That isn't mine

Moves shadows underneath the trees
Too tall, too thin, too tiny to be me

Spreads bindweed out to catch me
Flutters wild wings about my head
Tugs at my hair
But isn't there

And when I look
There's only the bend of grass
Where her running feet
Have smudged the dew

And there's only the sigh
Of her laughter
Trickling
Like
Moonlight
On
Wet
Weeds.

BERLIE DOHERTY

Legend

The blacksmith's boy went out with a rifle
and a black dog running behind.
Cobwebs snatched at his feet,
rivers hindered him,
thorn branches caught at his eyes to make him blind
and the sky turned into an unlucky opal,
but he didn't mind,
I can break branches, I can swim rivers, I can stare out any
    spider I meet,
said he to his dog and his rifle.

The blacksmith's boy went over the paddocks
with his old black hat on his head.
Mountains jumped in his way,
rocks rolled down on him,
and the old crow cried, You'll soon be dead.
And the rain came down like mattocks.
But he only said
I can climb mountains, I can dodge rocks, I can shoot an
    old crow any day,
and he went on over the paddocks.

When he came to the end of the day the sun began falling.
Up came the night ready to swallow him,
like the barrel of the gun,
like an old black hat,
like a black dog hungry to follow him.
Then the pigeon, the magpie and the dove began wailing
and the grass lay down to billow him.
His rifle broke, his hat flew away and his dog was gone
and the sun was falling.

But in front of the night the rainbow stood on a mountain,
just as his heart foretold.
He ran like a hare,
he climbed like a fox;
he caught it in his hands, the colour and the cold—
like a bar of ice, like the column of a fountain,
like a ring of gold.
The pigeon, the magpie and the dove flew to stare,
And the grass stood up again on the mountain.

The blacksmith's boy hung the rainbow on his shoulder
instead of his broken gun.
Lizards ran out to see,
snakes made way for him,
and the rainbow shone as brightly as the sun.
All the world said, Nobody is braver, nobody is bolder,
Nobody else has done
anything to equal it. He went home as bold as he could be
with the swinging rainbow on his shoulder.

JUDITH WRIGHT

A Small Dragon

I've found a small dragon in the woodshed.
Think it must have come from deep inside a forest
because it's damp and green and leaves
are still reflecting in its eyes.

I fed it on many things, tried grass,
the roots of stars, hazel-nut and dandelion,
but it stared up at me as if to say, I need
foods you can't provide.

It made a nest among the coal,
not unlike a bird's but larger,
it is out of place here
and is quite silent.

If you believed in it I would come
hurrying to your house to let you share my wonder,
but I want instead to see
if you yourself will pass this way.

BRIAN PATTEN

The Tale of Custard the Dragon

Belinda lived in a little white house,
With a little black kitten and a little gray mouse,
And a little yellow dog and a little red wagon,
And a realio, trulio, little pet dragon.

Now the name of the little black kitten was Ink,
And the little gray mouse, she called her Blink,
And the little yellow dog was sharp as Mustard,
But the dragon was a coward, and she called him Custard.

Custard the dragon had big sharp teeth,
And spikes on top of him and scales underneath,
Mouth like a fireplace, chimney for a nose,
And realio, trulio daggers on his toes.

Belinda was as brave as a barrel full of bears,
And Ink and Blink chased lions down the stairs,
Mustard was as brave as a tiger in a rage,
But Custard cried for a nice safe cage.

Belinda tickled him, she tickled him unmerciful,
Ink, Blink and Mustard, they rudely called him Percival,
They all sat laughing in the little red wagon
At the realio, trulio, cowardly dragon.

Belinda giggled till she shook the house,
And Blink said Weeck! which is giggling for a mouse,
Ink and Mustard rudely asked his age,
When Custard cried for a nice safe cage.

Suddenly, suddenly they heard a nasty sound,
And Mustard growled, and they all looked around.
Meowch! cried Ink, and Ooh! cried Belinda,
For there was a pirate, climbing in the winda.

Pistol in his left hand, pistol in his right,
And he held in his teeth a cutlass bright,
His beard was black, one leg was wood;
It was clear that the pirate meant no good.

Belinda paled, and she cried Help! Help!
But Mustard fled with a terrified yelp,
Ink trickled down to the bottom of the household,
And little mouse Blink strategically mouseholed.

But up jumped Custard, snorting like an engine,
Clashed his tail like irons in a dungeon,
With a clatter and a clank and a jangling squirm
He went at the pirate like a robin at a worm.

The pirate gaped at Belinda's dragon,
And gulped some grog from his pocket flagon,
He fired two bullets, but they didn't hit,
And Custard gobbled him, every bit.

Belinda embraced him, Mustard licked him,
No one mourned for his pirate victim.
Ink and Blink in glee did gyrate
Around the dragon that ate the pyrate.

Belinda still lives in her little white house,
With her little black kitten and her little gray mouse,
And her little yellow dog and her little red wagon,
And her realio, trulio, little pet dragon.

Belinda is as brave as a barrel full of bears,
And Ink and Blink chase lions down the stairs.
Mustard is as brave as a tiger in a rage,
But Custard keeps crying for a nice safe cage.

OGDEN NASH

Witches' Song

Round about the cauldron go;
In the poison'd entrails throw.
Toad, that under cold stone
Days and nights has thirty-one
Swelter'd venom, sleeping got,
Boil thou first i'th'charmed pot.
Double, double toil and trouble:
Fire, burn; and cauldron, bubble.
Fillet of a fenny snake,
In the cauldron boil and bake;
Eye of newt, and toe of frog,
Wool of bat, and tongue of dog,
Adder's fork, and blind-worm's sting,
Lizard's leg, and howlet's wing,
For a charm of powerful trouble,
Like a hell-broth boil and bubble.
Double, double toil and trouble:
Fire burn; and cauldron, bubble.

WILLIAM SHAKESPEARE

The Garden's Full of Witches

Mum! The garden's full of witches!
Come quick and see the witches,
  There's a full moon out,
  And they're flying about,
Come on! You'll miss the witches.

Oh Mum! You're missing the witches.
You have never seen so many witches.
  They're casting spells!
  There are horrible smells!
Come on! You'll miss the witches.

Mum, hurry! Come look at the witches.
The shrubbery's bursting with witches.
  They've turned our Joan
  Into a garden gnome.
Come on! You'll miss the witches.

Oh no! You'll miss the witches.
The garden's black with witches.
  Come on! Come on!
  Too late! They've gone.
Oh, you always miss the witches!

COLIN MCNAUGHTON

Jamjar

A girl in her garden peeped into a jamjar and fell inside.
She passed a wasp as she fell, it was licking
a smear of strawberry jam from the rim of the jar.
How far is the bottom? she cried as she fell.
Far, very far, drawled the wasp, *terribly far*.

Down she fell. The jar was a bell and her scream
was its tinkly, echoing ring. A green caterpillar
crawled up the outside glass of the jar, blinked
with its bulging alien eyes. *Help!* screeched the girl. *Help!*
Alas, it lisped, *there's no help in the whole wide world*.

On she hurled, into the well of the jar, till the opening
was a tiny star and dandelion clocks were silver planets
spinning in space. A spider hung from a thread
and peered at her face. *Throw me a rope!* she begged.
Not here, not now, it sneered, *nor any time or place*.

Bump. The jamjar's floor was snow and ice, stretching
for freezing miles. The girl skated away, all alone,
calling for home. White wolves ran in her tracks
under the hard stars. *Show me the way*, she sobbed.
No way to show, they howled, *and no way back*.

Then a hand picked up the jar; a mean squint eye swam
like a needlefish to the glass; poisonous breath clouded it over.
This will do for a vase, said a spiteful voice, as a Witch
filled up the jamjar with water, then stared in amazed,
glee in her eyes, at her swimming and brand new creature.

CAROL ANN DUFFY

The Hag

The Hag is astride,
This night for to ride;
The Devil and she together;
Through thick and through thin,
Now out and then in,
Though ne'er so foul be the weather.

A thorn or a burr
She takes for a spur,
With a lash of a bramble she rides now;
Through brakes and through briars,
O'er ditches and mires,
She follows the Spirit that guides now.

No Beast for his food
Dares now range the wood,
But hushed in his lair he lies lurking;
While mischiefs, by these,
On land and on seas,
At noon of night are a-working.

The storm will arise
And trouble the skies;
This night, and more for the wonder,
The ghost from the tomb
Affrighted shall come,
Called out by the clap of the thunder.

ROBERT HERRICK

The Visitor

it came today to visit
and moved into the house
it was smaller than an elephant
but larger than a mouse

first it slapped my sister
then it kicked my dad
then it pushed my mother
oh! that really made me mad

it went and tickled rover
and terrified the cat
it sliced apart my necktie
and rudely crushed my hat

it smeared my head with honey
and filled the tub with rocks
and when i yelled in anger
it stole my shoes and socks

that's just the way it happened
it happened all today
before it bowed politely
and softly went away

JACK PRELUTSKY

That Old Haunted House

That old haunted house was so creepy, so crawly, so
ghastly, so ghostly, so gruesome, so skully-and-bony.
That old haunted house gave me nightmares and
daymares and shudders and shivers and quivers and
quavers and quakes.
That old haunted house made my hair stand on end and
my heart pound-pound-pound and the blood in my
veins ice-cold-freezing.
That old haunted house gave me goose bumps and
throat lumps and ch-ch-ch-chattering teeth and the
sh-sh-sh-shakes.
That old haunted house made me shriek, made me eeek,
made me faint, made me scared-to-death scared,
made me all-over sweat.
Would I ever go back to that old haunted house?

You bet.

JUDITH VIORST

The Hairy Toe

Once there was a woman went out to pick beans,
and she found a Hairy Toe.
She took the Hairy Toe home with her,
and that night, when she went to bed,
the wind began to moan and groan.
Away off in the distance
she seemed to hear a voice crying,
'Where's my Hair-r-ry To-o-e?
Who's got my Hair-r-ry To-o-e?'

The woman scrooched down,
way down under the covers,
and about that time
the wind appeared to hit the house,

smoosh,

and the old house creaked and cracked
like something was trying to get in.
The voice had come nearer,
almost at the door now,
and it said,
'Where's my Hair-r-ry To-o-e?
Who's got my Hair-r-ry To-o-e?'

The woman scrooched further down
under the covers
and pulled them tight around her head.

The wind growled around the house
like some big animal
and r-r-um-umbled
over the chimbley.
All at once she heard the door cr-r-a-ack
and Something slipped in
and began to creep over the floor.

The floor went
cre-e-eak, cre-e-eak
at every step that thing took towards her bed.
The woman could almost feel
it bending over her bed.
There in an awful voice it said:
'Where's my Hair-r-ry To-o-e?
Who's got my Hair-r-ry To-o-e?
You've got it!'

TRADITIONAL

The Dark House

In a dark, dark wood, there was a dark, dark house,
And in that dark, dark house, there was a dark, dark room,
And in that dark, dark room, there was a dark, dark cupboard,
And in that dark, dark cupboard, there was a dark, dark shelf,
And in that dark, dark shelf, there was a dark, dark box,
And in that dark, dark box, there was a GHOST!

ANON.

The Highwayman

Part One

The wind was a torrent of darkness among the gusty trees,
The moon was a ghostly galleon tossed upon cloudy seas,
The road was a ribbon of moonlight over the purple moor,
And the highwayman came riding—
    Riding—riding—
The highwayman came riding, up to the old inn-door.

He'd a French cocked-hat on his forehead, a bunch of lace
  at his chin,
A coat of the claret velvet, and breeches of brown doe-skin;
They fitted with never a wrinkle: his boots were up to the thigh!
And he rode with a jewelled twinkle,
    His pistol butts a-twinkle,
His rapier hilt a-twinkle, under the jewelled sky.

Over the cobbles he clattered and clashed in the dark inn-yard,
And he tapped with his whip on the shutters, but all was
  locked and barred;
He whistled a tune to the window, and who should be
  waiting there
But the landlord's black-eyed daughter,
    Bess, the landlord's daughter,
Plaiting a dark red love-knot into her long black hair.

And dark in the dark old inn-yard a stable-wicket creaked
Where Tim the ostler listened; his face was white and peaked;
His eyes were hollows of madness, his hair like mouldy hay,
But he loved the landlord's daughter,
    The landlord's red-lipped daughter.
Dumb as a dog he listened, and he heard the robber say—

'One kiss, my bonny sweetheart, I'm after a prize to-night,
But I shall be back with the yellow gold before the
  morning light;
Yet, if they press me sharply, and harry me through the day,
Then look for me by moonlight,
    Watch for me by moonlight,
I'll come to thee by moonlight, though hell should bar the way.'

He rose upright in the stirrups; he scarce could reach her hand,
But she loosened her hair i' the casement! His face burnt like
  a brand
As the black cascade of perfume came tumbling over his breast;
And he kissed its waves in the moonlight,
    (Oh, sweet, black waves in the moonlight!)
Then he tugged at his rein in the moonlight, and galloped
  away to the west.

Part Two

He did not come in the dawning; he did not come at noon;
And out o' the tawny sunset, before the rise o' the moon,
When the road was a gypsy's ribbon, looping the purple moor,
A red-coat troop came marching—
        Marching—marching—
King George's men came marching, up to the old inn-door.

They said no word to the landlord, they drank his ale instead,
But they gagged his daughter and bound her to the foot of
    her narrow bed;
Two of them knelt at her casement, with muskets at their side!
There was death at every window;
        And hell at one dark window;
For Bess could see, through her casement, the road that *he*
    would ride.

They had tied her up to attention, with many a sniggering jest;
They had bound a musket beside her, with the barrel
    beneath her breast!
'Now, keep good watch!' and they kissed her.
        She heard the dead man say—
Look for me by moonlight;
        Watch for me by moonlight;
I'll come to thee by moonlight, though hell should bar the way!

She twisted her hands behind her; but all the knots held good!
She writhed her hands till her fingers were wet with sweat or
blood!
They stretched and strained in the darkness, and the hours
crawled by like years,
Till, now, on the stroke of midnight,
Cold, on the stroke of midnight,
The tip of one finger touched it! The trigger at least was hers!

The tip of one finger touched it; she strove no more for the rest.
Up, she stood up to attention, with the barrel beneath her breast.
She would not risk their hearing; she would not strive again;
For the road lay bare in the moonlight;
Blank and bare in the moonlight;
And the blood of her veins in the moonlight throbbed to her
love's refrain.

Tlot-tlot; tlot-tlot! Had they heard it? The horse-hoofs ringing
clear;
Tlot-tlot, tlot-tlot, in the distance! Were they deaf that they did
not hear?
Down the ribbon of moonlight, over the brow of the hill,
The highwayman came riding,
Riding, riding!
The red-coats looked to their priming! She stood up, straight
and still!

Tlot-tlot, in the frosty silence! *Tlot-tlot*, in the echoing night!
Nearer he came and nearer! Her face was like a light!
Her eyes grew wide for a moment; she drew one last deep
  breath,
Then her finger moved in the moonlight,
    Her musket shattered the moonlight,
Shattered her breast in the moonlight and warned him—
  with her death.

He turned; he spurred to the west; he did not know who stood
Bowed, with her head o'er the musket, drenched with her
  own red blood!
Not till the dawn he heard it, his face grew grey to hear
How Bess, the landlord's daughter,
    The landlord's black-eyed daughter,
Had watched for her love in the moonlight, and died in
  the darkness there.

Back, he spurred like a madman, shrieking a curse to the sky,
With the white road smoking behind him and his rapier
  brandished high!
Blood-red were his spurs i' the golden noon; wine-red was
  his velvet coat,
When they shot him down on the highway,
    Down like a dog on the highway,
And he lay in his blood on the highway, with the bunch of
  lace at his throat.

And still of a winter's night, they say, when the wind is in the trees,
When the moon is a ghostly galleon tossed upon cloudy seas,
When the road is a ribbon of moonlight over the purple moor,
A highwayman comes riding—
Riding—riding—
A highwayman comes riding, up to the old inn-door.

Over the cobbles he clatters and clangs in the dark inn-yard,
He taps with his whip on the shutters, but all is locked and barred;
He whistles a tune to the window, and who should be waiting there
But the landlord's black-eyed daughter,
Bess, the landlord's daughter,
Plaiting a dark red love-knot into her long black hair.

ALFRED NOYES

The Listeners

'Is there anybody there?' said the Traveller,
   Knocking on the moonlit door;
And his horse in the silence champed the grasses
   Of the forest's ferny floor:
And a bird flew up out of the turret,
   Above the Traveller's head:
And he smote upon the door again a second time;
   'Is there anybody there?' he said.
But no one descended to the Traveller;
   No head from the leaf-fringed sill
Leaned over and looked into his grey eyes,
   Where he stood perplexed and still.
But only a host of phantom listeners
   That dwelt in the lone house then
Stood listening in the quiet of the moonlight
   To that voice from the world of men:
Stood thronging the faint moonbeams on the dark stair,
   That goes down to the empty hall,
Hearkening in an air stirred and shaken
   By the lonely Traveller's call.
And he felt in his heart their strangeness,
   Their stillness answering his cry,
While his horse moved, cropping the dark turf,
   'Neath the starred and leafy sky;
For he suddenly smote on the door, even
   Louder, and lifted his head:—
'Tell them I came, and no one answered,
   That I kept my word,' he said.
Never the least stir made the listeners,
   Though every word he spake

Fell echoing through the shadowiness of the still house
   From the one man left awake:
Ay, they heard his foot upon the stirrup,
   And the sound of iron on stone,
And how the silence surged softly backward,
   When the plunging hoofs were gone.

WALTER DE LA MARE

Kubla Khan

In Xanadu did Kubla Khan
  A stately pleasure-dome decree:
Where Alph, the sacred river, ran
Through caverns measureless to man
  Down to a sunless sea.
So twice five miles of fertile ground
With walls and towers were girdled round:
And here were gardens bright with sinuous rills,
Where blossomed many an incense-bearing tree;
And here were forests ancient as the hills,
Enfolding sunny spots of greenery.

But Oh! that deep romantic chasm which slanted
Down the green hill athwart a cedarn cover!
A savage place! as holy and enchanted
As e'er beneath a waning moon was haunted
By woman wailing for her demon-lover!
And from this chasm, with ceaseless turmoil seething,
As if this Earth in fast thick pants were breathing,
A might fountain momently was forced:
Amid whose swift half-intermitted burst
Huge fragments vaulted like rebounding hail,
Or chaffy grain beneath the thresher's flail:
And 'mid these dancing rocks at once and ever
It flung up momently the sacred river.
Five miles meandering with a mazy motion
Through wood and dale the sacred river ran,
Then reached the caverns measureless to man,
And sank in tumult to a lifeless ocean:
And 'mid this tumult Kubla heard from far

Ancestral voices prophesying war!
    The shadow of the dome of pleasure
    Floated midway on the waves;
    Where was heard the mingled measure
    From the fountain and the caves.
It was a miracle of rare device,
A sunny pleasure-dome with caves of ice!

    A damsel with a dulcimer
    In a vision once I saw:
    It was an Abyssinian maid,
    And on her dulcimer she played,
    Singing of Mount Abora.
Could I revive within me
Her symphony and song,
To such a deep delight 'twould win me
That with music loud and long,
I would build that dome in air,
That sunny dome! those caves of ice!
And all who heard should see them there,
And all should cry, Beware! Beware!
His flashing eyes, his floating hair!
Weave a circle round him thrice,
And close your eyes with holy dread,
For he on honey-dew hath fed,
And drunk the milk of Paradise.

SAMUEL TAYLOR COLERIDGE

The Pied Piper of Hamelin

Hamelin Town's in Brunswick,
By famous Hanover city;
The river Weser, deep and wide,
Washes its wall on the southern side;
A pleasanter spot you never spied;
But, when begins my ditty,
Almost five hundred years ago,
To see the townsfolk suffer so
From vermin, was a pity.

Rats!
They fought the dogs, and killed the cats,
And bit the babies in the cradles,
And ate the cheeses out of the vats,
And licked the soup from the cooks' own ladles,
Split open the kegs of salted sprats,
Made nests inside men's Sunday hats,
And even spoiled the women's chats,
By drowning their speaking
With shrieking and squeaking
In fifty different sharps and flats.

At last the people in a body
To the Town Hall came flocking:
''Tis clear,' cried they, 'our Mayor's a noddy;
And as for our Corporation—shocking
To think we buy gowns lined with ermine
For dolts that can't or won't determine
What's best to rid us of our vermin!
You hope, because you're old and obese,
To find in the furry civic robe ease?

Rouse up, Sirs! Give your brains a racking
To find the remedy we're lacking,
Or, sure as fate, we'll send you packing!'
At this the Mayor and Corporation
Quaked with a mighty consternation.

An hour they sate in council,
At length the Mayor broke silence:
'For a guilder I'd my ermine gown sell;
I wish I were a mile hence!
It's easy to bid one rack one's brain—
I'm sure my poor head aches again
I've scratched it so, and all in vain.
Oh for a trap, a trap, a trap!'
Just as he said this, what should hap
At the chamber door but a gentle tap?
'Bless us,' cried the Mayor, 'what's that?'
(With the Corporation as he sat,
Looking little though wondrous fat;
Nor brighter was his eye, nor moister
Than a too-long-opened oyster,
Save when at noon his paunch grew mutinous
For a plate of turtle green and glutinous)
'Only a scraping of shoes on the mat?
Anything like the sound of a rat
Makes my heart go pit-a-pat!'

'Come in!'—the Mayor cried, looking bigger:
And in did come the strangest figure!
His queer long coat from heel to head
Was half of yellow and half of red;
And he himself was tall and thin,
With sharp blue eyes, each like a pin,

And light loose hair, yet swarthy skin,
No tuft on cheek nor beard on chin,
But lips where smiles went out and in—
There was no guessing his kith and kin!
And nobody could enough admire
The tall man and his quaint attire:
Quoth one: 'It's as my great-grandsire,
Starting up at the Trump of Doom's tone,
Had walked this way from his painted tomb-stone!'

He advanced to the council-table:
And, 'Please your honours,' said he, 'I'm able
By means of a secret charm to draw
All creatures living beneath the sun,
That creep or swim or fly or run,
After me so as you never saw!
And I chiefly use my charm
On creatures that do people harm,
The mole and toad and newt and viper;
And people call me the Pied Piper.'
(And here they noticed round his neck
A scarf of red and yellow stripe,
To match with his coat of the self-same cheque;
And at the scarf's end hung a pipe;
And his fingers, they noticed, were ever straying
As if impatient to be playing
Upon this pipe, as low it dangled
Over his vesture so old-fangled.)
'Yet,' said he, 'poor piper as I am,
In Tartary I freed the Cham,
Last June, from his huge swarms of gnats;
I eased in Asia the Nizam

Of a monstrous brood of vampire-bats:
And as for what your brain bewilders,
If I can rid your town of rats
Will you give me a thousand guilders?'
'One? fifty thousand!'—was the exclamation
Of the astonished Mayor and Corporation.

Into the street the Piper stept,
Smiling first a little smile,
As if he knew what magic slept
In his quiet pipe the while;
Then, like a musical adept,
To blow the pipe his lips he wrinkled,
And green and blue his sharp eyes twinkled
Like a candle-flame where salt is sprinkled;
And ere three shrill notes the pipe uttered,
You heard as if an army muttered;
And the muttering grew to a grumbling;
And the grumbling grew to a mighty rumbling;
And out of the houses the rats came tumbling.
Great rats, small rats, lean rats, brawny rats,
Brown rats, black rats, grey rats, tawny rats,
Grave old plodders, gay young friskers,
Fathers, mothers, uncles, cousins,
Cocking tails and pricking whiskers,
Families by tens and dozens,
Brothers, sisters, husbands, wives—
Followed the Piper for their lives.
From street to street he piped advancing,
And step for step they followed dancing,
Until they came to the river Weser
Wherein all plunged and perished!

—Save one who, stout as Julius Caesar,
Swam across and lived to carry
(As he, the manuscript he cherished)
To Rat-land home his commentary:
Which was, 'At the first shrill notes of the pipe,
I heard a sound as of scraping tripe,
And putting apples, wondrous ripe,
Into a cider-press's gripe:
And a moving away of pickle-tub boards,
And a leaving ajar of conserve-cupboards,
And a drawing the corks of train-oil flasks,
And a breaking the hoops of butter-casks;
And it seemed as if a voice
(Sweeter far than by harp or by psaltery
Is breathed) called out, Oh rats, rejoice!
The world is grown to one vast dry-saltery!
So, munch on, crunch on, take your nuncheon,
Breakfast, supper, dinner, luncheon!
And just as a bulky sugar-puncheon,
All ready staved, like a great sun shone
Glorious scarce an inch before me,
Just as methought it said, Come, bore me!
—I found the Weser rolling o'er me.'

You should have heard the Hamelin people
Ringing the bells till they rocked the steeple.
'Go,' cried the Mayor, 'and get long poles!
Poke out the nests and block up the holes!
Consult with carpenters and builders,
And leave in our town not even a trace
Of the rats!'—when suddenly, up the face
Of the Piper perked in the market-place,

With a 'First, if you please, my thousand guilders!'

A thousand guilders! The Mayor looked blue;
So did the Corporation too.
For council dinners made rare havoc
With Claret, Moselle, Vin-de-Grave, Hock;
And half the money would replenish
Their cellar's biggest butt with Rhenish.
To pay this sum to a wandering fellow
With a gipsy coat of red and yellow!
'Beside,' quoth the Mayor with a knowing wink,
'Our business was done at the river's brink;
We saw with our eyes the vermin sink,
And what's dead can't come to life, I think.
So, friend, we're not the folks to shrink
From the duty of giving you something to drink,
And a matter of money to put in your poke;
But as for the guilders, what we spoke
Of them, as you very well know, was in joke.
Besides, our losses have made us thrifty,
A thousand guilders! Come, take fifty!'

The Piper's face fell, and he cried,
'No trifling! I can't wait. Beside,
I've promised to visit by dinner time
Bagdad, and accept the prime
Of the Head-Cook's pottage, all he's rich in,
For having left, in the Caliph's kitchen,
Of a nest of scorpions no survivor—
With him I proved no bargain-driver,
With you, don't think I'll bate a stiver!
And folks who put me in a passion
May find me pipe to another fashion.'

'How?' cried the Mayor, 'd'ye think I'll brook
Being worse treated than a Cook?
Insulted by a lazy ribald
With idle pipe and vesture piebald?
You threaten us, fellow? Do your worst,
Blow your pipe there till you burst!'

Once more he stept into the street;
And to his lips again
Laid his long pipe of smooth straight cane;
And ere he blew three notes (such sweet
Soft notes as yet musician's cunning
Never gave the enraptured air)
There was a rustling, that seemed like a bustling
Of merry crowd jostling at pitching and hustling,
Small feet were pattering, wooden shoes clattering,
Little hands clapping and little tongues chattering,
And, like fowls in a farm-yard when barley is scattering,
Out came the children running.
All the little boys and girls,
With rosy cheeks and flaxen curls,
And sparkling eyes and teeth like pearls,
Tripping and skipping, ran merrily after
The wonderful music with shouting and laughter.

The Mayor was dumb, and the Council stood
As if they were changed into blocks of wood,
Unable to move a step, or cry
To the children merrily skipping by—
And could only follow with the eye
That joyous crowd at the Piper's back.
But how the Mayor was on the rack,
And the wretched Council's bosoms beat,

As the Piper turned from the High Street
To where the Weser rolled its waters
Right in the way of their sons and daughters!

However he turned from South to West,
And to Koppelberg Hill his steps addressed,
And after him the children pressed;
Great was the joy in every breast.
'He never can cross that mighty top!
He's forced to let the piping drop,
And we shall see our children stop!'
When, lo, as they reached the mountain's side,
A wondrous portal opened wide,
As if a cavern was suddenly hollowed;
And the Piper advanced and the children followed,
And when all were in to the very last,
The door in the mountain-side shut fast.
Did I say, all? No! One was lame,
And could not dance the whole of the way;
And in after years, if you would blame
His sadness, he was used to say,—
'It's dull in our town since my playmates left!
I can't forget that I'm bereft
Of all the pleasant sights they see,
Which the Piper also promised me.
For he led us, he said, to a joyous land,
Joining the town and just at hand,
Where waters gushed and fruit-trees grew,
And flowers put forth a fairer hue,
And everything was strange and new;
The sparrows were brighter than peacocks here,
And their dogs outran our fallow deer,

And honey-bees had lost their stings,
And horses were born with eagles' wings:
And just as I became assured
My lame foot would be speedily cured,
The music stopped and I stood still,
And found myself outside the Hill,
Left alone against my will,
To go now limping as before,
And never hear of that country more!'

Alas, alas for Hamelin!
There came into many a burgher's pate
A text which says, that Heaven's Gate
Opes to the Rich at as easy rate
As the needle's eye takes a camel in!
The Mayor sent East, West, North and South,
To offer the Piper, by word of mouth,
Wherever it was men's lot to find him,
Silver and gold to his heart's content,
If he'd only return the way he went,
And bring the children behind him.
But when they saw 'twas a lost endeavour,
And Piper and dancers were gone for ever,
They made a decree that lawyers never
Should think their records dated duly
If, after the day of the month and year,
These words did not as well appear,
'And so long after what happened here
On the Twenty-second of July,
Thirteen-hundred and seventy-six':
And the better in memory to fix
The place of the children's last retreat,

They called it, the Pied Piper's Street—
Where any one playing on pipe or tabor
Was sure for the future to lose his labour
Nor suffered they hostelry or tavern
To shock with mirth a street so solemn;
But opposite the place of the cavern
They wrote the story on a column,
And on the great Church-Window painted
The same, to make the world acquainted
How their children were stolen away;
And there it stands to this very day.

And I must not omit to say
That in Transylvania there's a tribe
Of alien people that ascribe
The outlandish ways and dress
On which their neighbours lay such stress
To their fathers and mothers having risen
Out of some subterraneous prison
Into which they were trepanned
Long time ago in a mighty band
Out of Hamelin town in Brunswick land,
But how or why, they don't understand.

Robert Browning

Eldorado

Gaily bedight,
A gallant knight,
In sunshine and in shadow,
Had journeyed long,
Singing a song,
In search of Eldorado.

But he grew old—
This knight so bold—
And o'er his heart a shadow
Fell as he found
No spot of ground
That looked like Eldorado.

And, as his strength
Failed him at length,
He met a pilgrim shadow—
'Shadow,' said he,
'Where can it be—
This land of Eldorado?'

'Over the Mountains
Of the Moon,
Down the Valley of the Shadow,
Ride, boldly ride,'
The shade replied—
'If you seek for Eldorado!'

EDGAR ALLAN POE

Advice to a Knight

Wear modest armour; and walk quietly
In woods, where any noise is treacherous.
Avoid dragons and deceptive maidens.

Be polite to other men in armour,
Especially the fierce ones, who are often strong.
Treat all old men as they might be magicians.

So you may come back from your wanderings,
Clink proud and stiff into the queen's court
To doff your helmet and expect her thanks.

The young queen is amused at your white hair,
Asks you to show your notched and rusty sword,
And orders extra straw for your bedding.

Tomorrow put on your oldest clothes,
Take a stout stick and set off again,
It's safer that way if no more rewarding.

T. H. JONES

La Belle Dame Sans Merci

'O what can ail thee, Knight-at-arms,
Alone and palely loitering?
The sedge is wither'd from the lake,
And no birds sing.

'O what can ail thee, Knight-at-arms,
So haggard and so woe-begone?
The squirrel's granary is full,
And the harvest's done.

'I see a lily on thy brow
With anguish moist and fever dew,
And on thy cheek a fading rose
Fast withereth too.'

'I met a lady in the meads
Full beautiful—a faery's child,
Her hair was long, her foot was light,
And her eyes were wild.

'I made a garland for her head,
And bracelets too, and fragrant zone;
She look'd at me as she did love,
And made sweet moan.

'I set her on my pacing steed,
And nothing else saw all day long,
For sidelong would she bend and sing
A faery's song.

'She found me roots of relish sweet,
And honey wild and manna dew,
And sure in language strange she said
"I love thee true."

'She took me to her elfin grot,
And there she wept and sigh'd full sore;
And there I shut her wild wild eyes
With kisses four.

'And there she lulled me asleep,
And there I dream'd—Ah! woe betide!
The latest dream I ever dream'd
On the cold hill's side.

'I saw pale kings and princes too,
Pale warriors, death-pale were they all:
Who cried—"La belle Dame sans merci
Hath thee in thrall!"

'I saw their starv'd lips in the gloam
With horrid warning gaped wide,
And I awoke and found me here
On the cold hill's side.

'And this is why I sojourn here
Alone and palely loitering,
Though the sedge is wither'd from the lake,
And no birds sing.'

JOHN KEATS

The Woman of Water

There once was a woman of water
Refused a Wizard her hand.
So he took the tears of a statue
And the weight from a grain of sand
And he squeezed the sap from a comet
And the height from a cypress tree
And he drained the dark from midnight
And he charmed the brains from a bee
And he soured the mixture with thunder
And he stirred it with ice from hell
And the woman of water drank it down
And she changed into a well.

There once was a woman of water
Who was changed into a well
And the well smiled up at the Wizard
And down down down that old Wizard fell . . .

ADRIAN MITCHELL

The Lady of Shalott

Part I

On either side the river lie
Long fields of barley and of rye,
That clothe the wold and meet the sky;
And thro' the field the road runs by
  To many-tower'd Camelot;
And up and down the people go,
Gazing where the lilies blow
Round an island there below,
  The island of Shalott.

Willows whiten, aspens quiver,
Little breezes dusk and shiver
Thro' the wave that runs for ever
By the island in the river
  Flowing down to Camelot.
Four gray walls, and four gray towers,
Overlook a space of flowers,
And the silent isle imbowers
  The Lady of Shalott.

By the margin, willow-veil'd,
Slide the heavy barges trail'd
By slow horses; and unhail'd
The shallop flitteth silken-sail'd
  Skimming down to Camelot:
But who hath seen her wave her hand?
Or at the casement seen her stand?
Or is she known in all the land,
  The Lady of Shalott?

Only reapers, reaping early
In among the bearded barley,
Hear a song that echoes cheerly
From the river winding clearly,
    Down to tower'd Camelot:
And by the moon the reaper weary,
Piling sheaves in uplands airy,
Listening, whispers ''Tis the fairy
    Lady of Shalott.'

Part II

There she weaves by night and day
A magic web with colours gay.
She has heard a whisper say,
A curse is on her if she stay
    To look down to Camelot.
She knows not what the curse may be,
And so she weaveth steadily,
And little other care hath she,
    The Lady of Shalott.

And moving thro' a mirror clear
That hangs before her all the year,
Shadows of the world appear.
There she sees the highway near
    Winding down to Camelot:
There the river eddy whirls,
And there the surly village-churls,
And the red cloaks of market girls,
    Pass onward from Shalott.

Sometimes a troop of damsels glad,
An abbot on an ambling pad,
Sometimes a curly shepherd-lad,
Or long-hair'd page in crimson clad,
  Goes by to tower'd Camelot;
And sometimes thro' the mirror blue
The knights come riding two and two:
She hath no loyal knight and true,
  The Lady of Shalott.

But in her web she still delights
To weave the mirror's magic sights,
For often thro' the silent nights
A funeral, with plumes and lights,
  And music, went to Camelot:
Or when the moon was overhead,
Came two young lovers lately wed;
'I am half sick of shadows,' said
  The Lady of Shalott.

Part III

A bow-shot from her bower-eaves,
He rode between the barley-sheaves,
The sun came dazzling thro' the leaves,
And flamed upon the brazen greaves
  Of bold Sir Lancelot.
A red-cross knight for ever kneel'd
To a lady in his shield,
That sparkled on the yellow field,
  Beside remote Shalott.

The gemmy bridle glitter'd free,
Like to some branch of stars we see
Hung in the golden Galaxy.
The bridle bells rang merrily
    As he rode down to Camelot:
And from his blazon'd baldric slung
A mighty silver bugle hung,
And as he rode his armour rung,
    Beside remote Shalott.

All in the blue unclouded weather
Thick-jewell'd shone the saddle-leather,
The helmet and the helmet-feather
Burn'd like one burning flame together,
    As he rode down to Camelot.
As often thro' the purple night,
Below the starry clusters bright,
Some bearded meteor, trailing light,
    Moves over still Shalott.

His broad clear brow in sunlight glow'd;
On burnish'd hooves his war-horse trode;
From underneath his helmet flow'd
His coal-black curls as on he rode,
    As he rode down to Camelot.
From the bank and from the river
He flash'd into the crystal mirror,
'Tirra lira,' by the river
    Sang Sir Lancelot.

She left the web, she left the loom,
She made three paces thro' the room,
She saw the water-lily bloom,
She saw the helmet and the plume,
    She look'd down to Camelot.

Out flew the web and floated wide;
The mirror crack'd from side to side;
'The curse is come upon me!' cried
The Lady of Shalott.

Part IV

In the stormy east-wind straining,
The pale yellow woods were waning,
The broad stream in his banks complaining,
Heavily the low sky raining
Over tower'd Camelot;
Down she came and found a boat
Beneath a willow left afloat,
And round about the prow she wrote
The Lady of Shalott.

And down the river's dim expanse—
Like some bold seer in a trance,
Seeing all his own mischance—
With a glassy countenance
Did she look to Camelot.
And at the closing of the day
She loosed the chain, and down she lay;
The broad stream bore her far away,
The Lady of Shalott.

Lying, robed in snowy white
That loosely flew to left and right—
The leaves upon her falling light—
Thro' the noises of the night
She floated down to Camelot:
And as the boat-head wound along
The willowy hills and fields among,
They heard her singing her last song,
The Lady of Shalott.

Heard a carol, mournful, holy,
Chanted loudly, chanted lowly,
Till her blood was frozen slowly,
And her eyes were darken'd wholly,
    Turn'd to tower'd Camelot;
For ere she reach'd upon the tide
The first house by the water-side,
Singing in her song she died,
    The Lady of Shalott.

Under tower and balcony,
By garden-wall and gallery,
A gleaming shape she floated by,
Dead-pale between the houses high,
    Silent into Camelot.
Out upon the wharfs they came,
Knight and burgher, lord and dame,
And round the prow they read her name,
    The Lady of Shalott.

Who is this? and what is here?
And in the lighted palace near
Died the sound of royal cheer;
And they cross'd themselves for fear,
    All the knights at Camelot:
But Lancelot mused a little space;
He said, 'She has a lovely face;
God in His mercy lend her grace,
    The Lady of Shalott.'

ALFRED TENNYSON

Lochinvar

O young Lochinvar is come out of the west,
Through all the wide Border his steed was the best;
And save his good broadsword he weapons had none,
He rode all unarm'd, and he rode all alone.
So faithful in love, and so dauntless in war,
There never was knight like the young Lochinvar.

He staid not for brake, and he stopp'd not for stone,
He swam the Eske river where ford there was none;
But ere he alighted at Netherby gate,
The bride had consented, the gallant came late:
For a laggard in love, and a dastard in war,
Was to wed the fair Ellen of brave Lochinvar.

So boldly he enter'd the Netherby Hall,
Among bride's-men, and kinsmen, and brothers, and all:
Then spoke the bride's father, his hand on his sword,
(For the poor craven bridegroom said never a word,)
'O come ye in peace here, or come ye in war,
Or to dance at our bridal, young Lord Lochinvar?'

'I long woo'd your daughter, my suit you denied;—
Love swells like the Solway, but ebbs like its tide—
And now am I come, with this lost love of mine
To lead but one measure, drink one cup of wine.
There are maidens in Scotland more lovely by far,
That would gladly be bride to the young Lochinvar.'

The bride kiss'd the goblet: the knight took it up,
He quaff'd off the wine, and he threw down the cup.
She look'd down to blush, and she look'd up to sigh,
With a smile on her lips, and a tear in her eye.
He took her soft hand, ere her mother could bar,—
'Now tread we a measure!' said young Lochinvar.

So stately his form, and so lovely her face,
That never a hall such a galliard did grace;
While her mother did fret, and her father did fume,
And the bridegroom stood dangling his bonnet and plume;
And the bride-maidens whisper'd, ''Twere better by far
To have match'd our fair cousin with young Lochinvar.'

One touch to her hand, and one word in her ear,
When they reach'd the hall-door, and the charger stood near;
So light to the croupe the fair lady he swung,
So light to the saddle before her he sprung!
'She is won! we are gone, over bank, bush, and scaur;
They'll have fleet steeds that follow,' quoth young Lochinvar.

There was mounting 'mong Graemes of the Netherby clan;
Forsters, Fenwicks, and Musgraves, they rode and they ran:
There was racing and chasing on Cannobie Lee,
But the lost bride of Netherby ne'er did they see.
So daring in love, and so dauntless in war,
Have ye e'er heard of gallant like young Lochinvar?

WALTER SCOTT

I Think
I Could
Turn and
Live with
Animals

Animals

I think I could turn and live with animals, they are so
placid and self-contained;
I stand and look at them long and long.

They do not sweat and whine about their condition;
They do not lie awake in the dark and weep for their sins;

They do not make me sick discussing their duty to God;
Not one is dissatisfied—not one is demented with the
mania of owning things;

Not one kneels to another, nor to his kind that lived
thousands of years ago;
Not one is respectable or industrious over the whole earth.

WALT WHITMAN

Animal Rights

Our cat
Won't use the cat-flap
Any more.
He's started to fight
For his Animal Rights
And insists
That he uses the door.

LINDSAY MACRAE

The Song of the Jellicles

Jellicle Cats come out tonight
Jellicle Cats come one come all:
The Jellicle Moon is shining bright—
Jellicles come to the Jellicle Ball.

Jellicle Cats are black and white,
Jellicle Cats are rather small;
Jellicle Cats are merry and bright,
And pleasant to hear when they caterwaul.
Jellicle Cats have cheerful faces,
Jellicle Cats have bright black eyes;
They like to practise their airs and graces
And wait for the Jellicle Moon to rise.

Jellicle Cats develop slowly,
Jellicle Cats are not too big;
Jellicle Cats are roly-poly,
They know how to dance a gavotte and a jig.
Until the Jellicle Moon appears
They make their toilette and take their repose:
Jellicles wash behind their ears,
Jellicles dry between their toes.

Jellicle Cats are white and black,
Jellicle Cats are of moderate size;
Jellicles jump like a jumping-jack,
Jellicle Cats have moonlit eyes.

They're quiet enough in the morning hours,
They're quiet enough in the afternoon,
Reserving their terpsichorean powers
To dance by the light of the Jellicle Moon.

Jellicle Cats are black and white,
Jellicle Cats (as I said) are small;
If it happens to be a stormy night
They will practise a caper or two in the hall.
If it happens the sun is shining bright
You would say they had nothing to do at all:
They are resting and saving themselves to be right
For the Jellicle Moon and the Jellicle Ball.

T. S. ELIOT

Bye, Cat

Cats.
Hate 'em.

All fur and fluff
and spit and eyes in the dark.

Hate them.
Grrr!

At least think I do.
Never caught one.

Always up trees,
or tops of walls,

or leering from windows,
milk on their whiskers,

slipping through hedges
and me on my lead—

always
out of reach.

Never caught one? Never?
A big dog like you? I don't believe a word of it!

OK, I tell a lie
(never told my best friend this).

Caught one once.
Surprised it in the garden.

Up I rushed,
all fangs and claws,

bark like a police siren
promising blue murder.

Didn't move, stupid thing.
Sat there blinking.

What can you do
when a cat won't fight back?

Lick her on the nose.
Bark, 'Got you, kitty.'

Retreat on tip-claw.
'Bye, cat. Bye, cat.'

BRIAN MORSE

Alley Cat

A bit of jungle in the street
He goes on velvet toes,
And slinking through the shadows, stalks
Imaginary foes.

ESTHER VALCK GEORGES

Mice

Mice
Find places
In places,

A dark
Hall behind
The hall,

Odd rooms
That other
Rooms hide:

A world
Inside
The wide world,

And space enough,
Even in
Small spaces.

VALERIE WORTH

The Prayer of the Mouse

I am so little and grey,
dear God,
how can You keep me in mind?
Always spied upon,
always chased.
Nobody ever gives me anything,
and I nibble meagrely at life.
Why do they reproach me with being a mouse?
Who made me but You?
I only ask to stay hidden.
Give me my hunger's pittance
safe from the claws
of that devil with green eyes.

Amen

CARMEN BERNOS DE GASZTOLD
translated by Rumer Godden

Anne and the Field-Mouse

We found a mouse in the chalk quarry today
In a circle of stones and empty oil drums
By the fag ends of a fire. There had been
A picnic there; he must have been after the crumbs.

Jane saw him first, a flicker of brown fur
In and out of the charred wood and chalk-white.
I saw him last, but not till we'd turned up
Every stone and surprised him into flight,

Though not far—little zigzag spurts from stone
To stone. Once, as he lurked in his hiding-place,
I saw his beady eyes uplifted to mine.
I'd never seen such terror in so small a face.

I watched, amazed and guilty. Beside us suddenly
A heavy pheasant whirred up from the ground,
Scaring us all; and, before we knew it, the mouse
Had broken cover, skimming away without a sound,

Melting into the nettles. We didn't go
Till I'd chalked in capitals on a rusty can:
THERE'S A MOUSE IN THOSE NETTLES. LEAVE
HIM ALONE. NOVEMBER 15th. ANNE.

IAN SERRAILLIER

Ar-a-rat

I know a rat on Ararat,
He isn't thin, he isn't fat
Never been chased by any cat
Not that rat on Ararat.
He's sitting high on a mountain breeze,
Never tasted any cheese,
Never chewed up any old hat,
Not that rat on Ararat.
He just sits alone on a mountain breeze,
Wonders why the trees are green,
Ponders why the ground is flat,
O that rat on Ararat.
His eyes like saucers, glow in the dark—
The last to slip from Noah's ark.

GRACE NICHOLS

Cows on the Beach

Two cows,
fed-up with grass, field, farmer,
barged through barbed wire
and found the beach.
Each mooed to each:
This is a better place to be,
a stretch of sand next to the sea,
this is the place for me.
And they stayed there all day,
strayed this way, that way,
over to rocks,
past discarded socks,
ignoring the few people they met
(it wasn't the high season yet).
They dipped hooves in the sea,
got wet up to the knee,
they swallowed pebbles and sand,
found them a bit bland,
washed them down with sea-water,
decided they really ought to
rest for an hour.
Both were sure
they'd never leave here.
Imagine, they'd lived so near
and never knew!

With a swapped moo
they sank into sleep,
woke to the yellow jeep
of the farmer
revving there
feet from the incoming sea.
This is no place for cows to be,
he shouted, and slapped them
with seaweed, all the way home.

MATTHEW SWEENEY

Noah and the Rabbit

'No land,' said Noah,
'There-is-not-any-land.
Oh, Rabbit, Rabbit, can't you understand?'

But Rabbit shook his head:
'Say it again,' he said;
'And slowly, please.
No good brown earth for burrows,
And no trees;
No wastes where vetch and rabbit-parsley grows,
No brakes, no bushes and no turnip rows,
No holt, no upland, meadowland or weald,
No tangled hedgerow and no playtime field?'

'No land at all—just water,' Noah replied,
And Rabbit sighed.
'For always, Noah?' he whispered, 'will there be
Nothing henceforth for ever but the sea?
Or will there come a day
When the green earth will call me back to play?'

Noah bowed his head:
'Some day . . . some day,' he said.

HUGH CHESTERMAN

We are Going to See the Rabbit

We are going to see the rabbit,
We are going to see the rabbit.
Which rabbit, people say?
Which rabbit, ask the children?
Which rabbit?
The only rabbit,
The only rabbit in England,
Sitting behind a barbed-wire fence
Under the floodlights, neon lights,
Sodium lights,
Nibbling grass
On the only patch of grass
In England, in England
(Except the grass by the hoardings
Which doesn't count.)
We are going to see the rabbit
And we must be there on time.

First we shall go by escalator,
Then we shall go by underground,
And then we shall go by motorway
And then by helicopterway,
And the last ten yards we shall have to go
On foot.

And now we are going
All the way to see the rabbit,
We are nearly there,
We are longing to see it,
And so is the crowd
Which is here in thousands

With mounted policemen
And big loudspeakers
And bands and banners,
And everyone has come a long way.
But soon we shall see it
Sitting and nibbling
The blades of grass
On the only patch of grass
In—but something has gone wrong!
Why is everyone so angry,
Why is everyone jostling
And slanging and complaining?

The rabbit has gone,
Yes, the rabbit has gone.
He has actually burrowed down into the earth
And made himself a warren, under the earth,
Despite all these people.
And what shall we do?
What *can* we do?

It is all a pity, you must be disappointed,
Go home and do something else for today,
Go home again, go home for today.
For you cannot hear the rabbit, under the earth,
Remarking rather sadly to himself, by himself,
As he rests in his warren, under the earth:
'It won't be long, they are bound to come,
They are bound to come and find me, even here.'

ALAN BROWNJOHN

The Walrus and the Carpenter

The sun was shining on the sea,
Shining with all his might:
He did his very best to make
The billows smooth and bright—
And this was odd, because it was
The middle of the night.

The moon was shining sulkily,
Because she thought the sun
Had got no business to be there
After the day was done—
'It's very rude of him,' she said,
'To come and spoil the fun!'

The sea was wet as wet could be,
The sands were dry as dry.
You could not see a cloud, because
No cloud was in the sky:
No birds were flying overhead—
There were no birds to fly.

The Walrus and the Carpenter
Were walking close at hand;
They wept like anything to see
Such quantities of sand:
'If this were only cleared away,'
They said, 'it would be grand!'

'If seven maids with seven mops
Swept it for half a year,
Do you suppose,' the Walrus said,
'That they could get it clear?'
'I doubt it,' said the Carpenter,
And shed a bitter tear.

'O Oysters, come and walk with us!'
The Walrus did beseech.
'A pleasant walk, a pleasant talk,
Along the briny beach:
We cannot do with more than four,
To give a hand to each.'

The eldest Oyster looked at him,
But never a word he said:
The eldest Oyster winked his eye,
And shook his heavy head—
Meaning to say he did not choose
To leave the oyster-bed.

But four young Oysters hurried up,
All eager for the treat:
Their coats were brushed, their faces washed,
Their shoes were clean and neat—
And this was odd, because, you know,
They hadn't any feet.

Four other Oysters followed them,
And yet another four;
And thick and fast they came at last,
And more, and more, and more—
All hopping through the frothy waves,
And scrambling to the shore.

The Walrus and the Carpenter
Walked on a mile or so,
And then they rested on a rock
Conveniently low:
And all the little Oysters stood
And waited in a row.

'The time has come,' the Walrus said,
'To talk of many things:
Of shoes—and ships—and sealing wax—
Of cabbages—and kings—
And why the sea is boiling hot—
And whether pigs have wings.'

'But wait a bit,' the Oysters cried,
'Before we have our chat;
For some of us are out of breath,
And all of us are fat!'
'No hurry!' said the Carpenter.
They thanked him much for that.

'A loaf of bread,' the Walrus said,
'Is what we chiefly need:
Pepper and vinegar besides
Are very good indeed—
Now, if you're ready, Oysters dear,
We can begin to feed.'

'But not on us!' the Oysters cried,
Turning a little blue.
'After such kindness, that would be
A dismal thing to do!'
'The night is fine,' the Walrus said,
'Do you admire the view?'

'It was so kind of you to come!
And you are very nice!'
The Carpenter said nothing but
'Cut us another slice:
I wish you were not quite so deaf—
I've had to ask you twice!'

'It seems a shame,' the Walrus said,
'To play them such a trick,
After we've brought them out so far,
And made them trot so quick!'
The Carpenter said nothing but
'The butter's spread too thick!'

'I weep for you,' the Walrus said:
'I deeply sympathize.'
With sobs and tears he sorted out
Those of the largest size,
Holding his pocket-handkerchief
Before his streaming eyes.

'O Oysters,' said the Carpenter,
'You've had a pleasant run!
Shall we be trotting home again?'
But answer came there none—
And this was scarcely odd, because
They'd eaten every one.

LEWIS CARROLL

The Owl and the Pussy-Cat

The Owl and the Pussy-cat went to sea
  In a beautiful pea-green boat,
They took some honey, and plenty of money,
  Wrapped up in a five-pound note.
The Owl looked up to the stars above,
  And sang to a small guitar,
'O lovely Pussy, O Pussy, my love,
  What a beautiful Pussy you are,
    You are,
    You are!
  What a beautiful Pussy you are!'

Pussy said to the Owl, 'You elegant fowl,
  How charmingly sweet you sing!
O let us be married! too long we have tarried:
  But what shall we do for a ring?'
They sailed away, for a year and a day,
  To the land where the Bong-tree grows;
And there in a wood a Piggy-wig stood,
  With a ring at the end of his nose,
    His nose,
    His nose,
  With a ring at the end of his nose.

'Dear Pig, are you willing to sell for one shilling
  Your ring?' Said the Piggy, 'I will.'
So they took it away, and were married next day
  By the Turkey who lives on the hill.

They dined on mince, and slices of quince,
Which they ate with a runcible spoon;
And hand in hand, on the edge of the sand,
They danced by the light of the moon,
The moon,
The moon,
They danced by the light of the moon.

EDWARD LEAR

The Farmer and the Queen

'She's coming,' the farmer said to the owl.
'Oh, what shall I, what shall I do?
Shall I bow when she comes?
Shall I twiddle my thumbs?'
  The owl asked, 'Who?'

'The Queen, the Queen, the royal Queen—
She'll pass the farm today.
Shall I salute?' he asked the horse.
  The horse said, 'Nay.'

'Shall I give her a gift?' he asked the wren.
'A lovely memento for her to keep?
An egg or a peach or an ear of corn?'
  The wren said, 'Cheap.'

'But should I curtsy or should I cheer?
Oh, here's her carriage now.
What should I do?' he asked the dog.
  The dog said, 'Bow.'

And so he did, and so she passed,
Oh, tra lala lala,
'She smiled, she did!' he told the sheep.
  The sheep said, 'Bah!'

SHEL SILVERSTEIN

'Quack!' Said the Billy-Goat

'Quack!' said the billy-goat,
  'Oink!' said the hen.
'Miaow!' said the little chick
  Running in the pen.

'Hobble-gobble!' said the dog.
  'Cluck!' said the sow.
'Tu-whit tu-whoo!' the donkey said.
  'Baa!' said the cow.

'Hee-haw!' the turkey cried.
  The duck began to moo.
All at once the sheep went,
  'Cock-a-doodle-doo!'

The owl coughed and cleared his throat
  And he began to bleat.
'Bow-wow!' said the cock
  Swimming in the leat.

'Cheep-cheep!' said the cat
  As she began to fly.
'Farmer's been and laid an egg—
  That's the reason why.'

CHARLES CAUSLEY

The Song of the Mischievous Dog

There are many who say that a dog has its day,
  And a cat has a number of lives;
There are others who think that a lobster is pink,
  And that bees never work in their hives.
There are fewer, of course, who insist that a horse
  Has a horn and two humps on its head,
And a fellow who jests that a mare can build nests
  Is as rare as a donkey that's red.
Yet in spite of all this, I have moments of bliss,
  For I cherish a passion for bones,
And though doubtful of biscuit, I'm willing to risk it,
  And I love to chase rabbits and stones.
But my greatest delight is to take a good bite
  At a calf that is plump and delicious;
And if I indulge in a bite at a bulge,
  Let's hope you won't think me too vicious.

DYLAN THOMAS

All the Dogs

You should have seen him—
he stood in the park and whistled,
underneath an oak tree,
and all the dogs came bounding up
and sat around him,
keeping their big eyes on him,
tails going like pendulums.
And there was one cocker pup
who went and licked his hand,
and a Labrador who whimpered
till the rest joined in.

Then he whistled a second time,
high-pitched as a stoat,
over all the shouted dog names
and whistles of owners,
till a flurry of paws
brought more dogs, panting,
as if they'd come miles,
and these too found space
on the flattened grass
to stare at the boy's
unmemorable face
which all the dogs found special.

MATTHEW SWEENEY

One of Our St Bernard Dogs Is Missing

A moot point
Whether I was going to
Make it.
I just had the strength
To ring the bell.

There were monks inside
And one of them
Eventually
Opened the door.

Oh
He said.
This is a bit of a turn-up
He said
For the book.
Opportune
He said
Your arriving at this particular
As it were
Moment.

You're dead right
I said
It was touch and go
Whether I could have managed
To keep going
For very much longer.

No
He said
The reason I used the word opportune

Is that
Not to put too fine a point on it
One of our St Bernard dogs is
Unfortunately
Missing.

Oh dear
I said
Not looking for me I hope.

No
He said
It went for a walk
And got lost in the snow.

Dreadful thing
I said
To happen.

Yes
He said
It is.

To
Of all creatures
I said
A St Bernard dog
That has devoted
Its entire
Life
To doing good
And helping
Others.

What I was actually thinking
He said
Since you happen to be
In a manner of speaking
Out there already
Is that
If you could
At all
See your way clear
To having a scout
Around
It would save one of us
Having to
If I can so put it
Turn out.

Ah
I said
That would
I suppose
Make a kind of sense.

Before you go
He said
If I can find it
You'd better
Here it is
Take this.

What is it?
I said.

It's a flask
He said
Of brandy.

Ah
I said.

For the dog
He said.

Good thinking
I said.

The drill
He said
When you find it
If you ever do
Is to lie down.

Right
I said
Will do.

Lie down on top of it
He said
To keep it warm
Till help arrives.

N. F. SIMPSON

The Common Cormorant

The common cormorant or shag
Lays eggs inside a paper bag.
The reason you will see no doubt
It is to keep the lightning out.
But what these unobservant birds
Have never noticed is that herds
Of wandering bears may come with buns
And steal the bags to hold the crumbs.

CHRISTOPHER ISHERWOOD

from 'Auguries of Innocence'

A Robin Redbreast in a cage
Puts all Heaven in a rage.

A Dove house filled with Doves and Pigeons
Shudders hell through all its regions.

A Dog starved at his master's gate
Predicts the ruin of the state.

A Horse misused upon the road
Calls to Heaven for human blood.

Each outcry of the hunted Hare
A fibre from the brain does tear.

A Skylark wounded in the wing,
A cherubin does cease to sing.

The Game Cock clipped and armed for fight
Does the rising sun affright.

Every Wolf's and Lion's howl
Raises from hell a human soul.

The wild Deer wand'ring here and there
Keeps the human soul from care.

The Lamb misused breeds public strife
And yet forgives the butcher's knife.

The Bat that flits at close of eve
Has left the brain that won't believe.

The Owl that calls upon the night
Speaks the unbeliever's fright.

William Blake

Horrible Song

The Crow is a wicked creature
  Crooked in every feature.
Beware, beware of the Crow!
When the bombs burst, he laughs, he shouts;
When guns go off, he roundabouts;
When the limbs start to fly and the blood starts to flow
  Ho Ho Ho
  He sings the Song of the Crow.

The Crow is a sudden creature
  Thievish in every feature.
Beware, beware of the Crow!
When the sweating farmers sleep
He levers the jewels from the heads of their sheep.
Die in a ditch, your own will go,
  Ho Ho Ho
  While he sings the Song of the Crow.

The Crow is a subtle creature
  Cunning in every feature.
Beware, beware of the Crow!
When sick folk tremble on their cots
He sucks their souls through the chimney pots,
They're dead and gone before they know,
  Ho Ho Ho
  And he sings the Song of the Crow.

The Crow is a lusty creature
  Gleeful in every feature.
Beware, beware of the Crow!
If he can't get your liver, he'll find an old rat
Or highway hedgehog hammered flat,
Any old rubbish to make him grow,
  Ho Ho Ho
  While he sings the Song of the Crow.

The Crow is a hardy creature
  Fire-proof in every feature.
Beware, beware of the Crow!
When Mankind's blasted to kingdom come
The Crow will dance and hop and drum
And into an old thigh-bone he'll blow
  Ho Ho Ho
  Singing the Song of the Crow.

TED HUGHES

Sergeant Brown's Parrot

Many policemen wear upon their shoulders
Cunning little radios. To pass away the time
They talk about the traffic to them, listen to the news,
And it helps them to Keep Down Crime.

But Sergeant Brown, he wears upon his shoulder
A tall green parrot as he's walking up and down
And all the parrot says is 'Who's-a-pretty-boy-then?'
'I am,' says Sergeant Brown.

KIT WRIGHT

Woodpecker

Woodpecker is rubber-necked
  But has a nose of steel.
He bangs his head against the wall
  And cannot even feel.

When Woodpecker's jack-hammer head
  Starts up its dreadful din
Knocking the dead bough double dead
  How do his eyes stay in?

Pity the poor dead oak that cries
  In terrors and in pains
But pity more Woodpecker's eyes
  And bouncing rubber brains.

TED HUGHES

The Duck

Behold the duck.
It does not cluck.
A cluck it lacks.
It quacks.
It is specially fond
Of a puddle or pond.
When it dines or sups,
It bottoms ups.

OGDEN NASH

Ducks Don't Shop in Sainsbury's

You can't get millet at Sainsbury's
and they don't sell grass or weed
it's a total dead loss
for heather and moss
and they don't stock sunflower seed.

They've got some fish in the freezer
but they're low on rats and mice
and you're out of luck
if you're a debonair duck
and you want to buy something nice

'cos none of their bread is stale
and they've stopped selling hay and straw.
Let's face it, if you were a duck in Sainsbury's,
you'd be heading for the exit door!

GARY BOSWELL

Good Morning, Mr Croco-doco-dile

Good Morning, Mr Croco-doco-dile,
And how are you today?
I like to see you croco-smoco-smile
In your croco-woco-way.

From the tip of your beautiful croco-toco-tail
To your croco-hoco-head
You seem to me so croco-stoco-still
As if you're croco-doco-dead.

Perhaps if I touch your croco-cloco-claw
Or your croco-snoco-snout,
Or get up close to your croco-joco-jaw
I shall very soon find out.

But suddenly I croco-soco-see
In your croco-oco-eye
A curious kind of croco-gloco-gleam,
So I just don't think I'll try.

Forgive me, Mr Croco-doco-dile
But it's time I was away.
Let's talk a little croco-woco-while
Another croco-doco-day.

CHARLES CAUSLEY

Don't Call Alligator Long-Mouth Till You Cross River

Call alligator long-mouth
call alligator saw-mouth
call alligator pushy-mouth
call alligator scissors-mouth
call alligator raggedy-mouth
call alligator bumpy-bum
call alligator all dem rude word
but better wait
                    till you cross river.

JOHN AGARD

The Frog

Be kind and tender to the Frog,
  And do not call him names,
As 'Slimy skin,' or 'Polly-wog,'
  Or likewise 'Ugly James,'
Or 'Gape-a-grin,' or 'Toad-gone-wrong,'
  Or 'Billy Bandy-knees':
The Frog is justly sensitive
  To epithets like these.
No animal will more repay
  A treatment kind and fair;
At least so lonely people say
Who keep a frog (and, by the way,
  They are extremely rare).

HILAIRE BELLOC

What a Wonderful Bird the Frog Are

What a wonderful bird the frog are:—
When he sit, he stand almost:
When he hop, he fly almost.
He ain't got no sense hardly:
He ain't got no tail either.
When he sit, he sit on what he ain't got—almost.

ANON.

a black dot

a black dot
a jelly tot

a scum-nail
a jiggle-tail

a leg-kicker
a sitting slicker

a panting puffer
a fly-snuffer

a high-hopper
a belly-flopper

a catalogue
        to make me
                FROG

LIBBY HOUSTON

Little Fish

The tiny fish enjoy themselves
in the sea.
Quick little splinters of life,
their little lives are fun to them
in the sea.

D. H. LAWRENCE

The Law of the Jungle

Now this is the Law of the Jungle—as old and as true as the sky;
And the Wolf that shall keep it may prosper, but the Wolf that shall break it must die.

As the creeper that girdles the tree-trunk the Law runneth forward and back—
For the strength of the Pack is the Wolf, and the strength of the Wolf is the Pack.

Wash daily from nose-tip to tail-tip; drink deeply, but never too deep;
And remember the night is for hunting, and forget not the day is for sleep.

The Jackal may follow the Tiger, but, Cub, when thy whiskers are grown,
Remember the Wolf is a Hunter—go forth and get food of thine own.

Keep peace with the Lords of the Jungle—the Tiger, the Panther, the Bear;
And trouble not Hathi the Silent, and mock not the Boar in his lair.

When Pack meets with Pack in the Jungle, and neither will go from the trail,
Lie down till the leaders have spoken—it may be fair words shall prevail.

When ye fight with a Wolf of the Pack, ye must fight him
alone and afar,
Lest others take part in the quarrel, and the Pack be
diminished by war.

The Lair of the Wolf is his refuge, and where he has made
him his home,
Not even the Head Wolf may enter, not even the Council
may come.

The Lair of the Wolf is his refuge, but where he has
digged it too plain,
The Council shall send him a message, and so he shall
change it again.

If ye kill before midnight, be silent, and wake not the
woods with your bay,
Lest ye frighten the deer from the crops, and the brothers
go empty away.

Ye may kill for yourselves, and your mates, and your cubs
as they need, and ye can;
But kill not for pleasure of killing, and *seven times never
kill Man*.

If ye plunder his Kill from a weaker, devour not all in thy pride;
Pack-Right is the right of the meanest; so leave him the
head and the hide.

The Kill of the Pack is the meat of the Pack. Ye must eat
where it lies;
And no one may carry away of that meat to his lair, or he dies.

The Kill of the Wolf is the meat of the Wolf. He may do
what he will,
But, till he has given permission, the Pack may not eat of
that Kill.

Cub-Right is the right of the Yearling. From all of his
Pack he may claim
Full-gorge when the killer has eaten; and none may refuse
him the same.

Lair-Right is the right of the Mother. From all of her year
she may claim
One haunch of each kill for her litter, and none may deny
her the same.

Cave-Right is the right of the Father—to hunt by himself
for his own:
He is freed of all calls to the Pack; he is judged by the
Council alone.

Because of his age and his cunning, because of his gripe
and his paw,
In all that the Law leaveth open, the word of the Head
Wolf is Law.

*Now these are the Laws of the Jungle, and many and mighty
are they;*
*But the head and the hoof of the Law and the haunch and the
hump is—Obey!*

RUDYARD KIPLING

Evidence of Elephants

If you had had just the bones to go on,
Only the bones,
Could you have guessed an elephant?
How could you know?

Oh, you could work out the size and so on
By measuring the bones,
But the vast flapping ears, that caked-mud grey,
They would not show.

Nor the trunk. From the skull you'd never guess
At that long swinging trunk,
Boneless and flexible, sensitive and beautiful,
Hanging in front,

Or lifted to blare like a trumpet, or to caress
Another elephant.
If I had only the bones to help me,
I think I'd be stumped.

GERARD BENSON

Zebra Question

I asked the zebra,
Are you black with white stripes?
Or white with black stripes?
And the zebra asked me,
Are you good with bad habits?
Or are you bad with good habits?
Are you noisy with quiet times?
Or are you quiet with noisy times?
Are you happy with some sad days?
Or are you sad with some happy days?
Are you neat with some sloppy ways?
Or are you sloppy with some neat ways?
And on and on and on and on
And on and on he went.
I'll never ask a zebra
About stripes
Again.

SHEL SILVERSTEIN

The Tyger

Tyger! Tyger! burning bright
In the forests of the night,
What immortal hand or eye
Could frame thy fearful symmetry?

In what distant deeps or skies
Burnt the fire of thine eyes?
On what wings dare he aspire?
What the hand dare seize the fire?

And what shoulder, and what art
Could twist the sinews of thy heart?
And, when thy heart began to beat,
What dread hand? and what dread feet?

What the hammer? what the chain?
In what furnace was thy brain?
What the anvil? what dread grasp
Dare its deadly terrors clasp?

When the stars threw down their spears,
And water'd heaven with their tears,
Did he smile his work to see?
Did he who made the Lamb make thee?

Tyger! Tyger! burning bright
In the forests of the night,
What immortal hand or eye
Dare frame thy fearful symmetry?

WILLIAM BLAKE

City Jungle

Here I am
In the jungle city.
Tigers, like cars
Chase our feet.
Wild birds,
Like children
Scream bitterly.
Elephants lumber around
Like buses,
Giraffes have necks
As tall as buildings
And the monkeys' chatter
Sounds like my sister's.

NICOLE TOWNSEND

My Telly

My telly eats people
especially on the news

Little people
with no shoes
Little people
with no food
Little people
crying
Little people
dying

My telly
eats people
If you don't
believe me
look inside
the belly
of my telly

JOHN AGARD

Hunger

This is hunger. An animal
all fangs and eyes.
It cannot be distracted or deceived.
It is not satisfied with one meal.
It is not content
with a lunch or dinner.
Always threatens blood.
Roars like a lion, squeezes like a boa,
thinks like a person.

The specimen before you
was captured in India (outskirts of Bombay)
but it exists in a more or less savage state
in many other places.

Please stand back.

NICALÁS GUILLÉN

Little Red Riding Hood and the Wolf

As soon as Wolf began to feel
That he would like a decent meal,
He went and knocked on Grandma's door.
When Grandma opened it, she saw
The sharp white teeth, the horrid grin,
And Wolfie said, 'May I come in?'
Poor Grandmamma was terrified,
'He's going to eat me up!' she cried.
And she was absolutely right.
He ate her up in one big bite.
But Grandmamma was small and tough,
And Wolfie wailed, 'That's not enough!
'I haven't yet begun to feel
'That I have had a decent meal!'
He ran around the kitchen yelping,
'I've *got* to have another helping!'
Then added with a frightful leer,
'I'm therefore going to wait right here
'Till Little Miss Red Riding Hood
'Comes home from walking in the wood.'
He quickly put on Grandma's clothes,
(Of course he hadn't eaten those.)

He dressed himself in coat and hat.
He put on shoes and after that
He even brushed and curled his hair,
Then sat himself in Grandma's chair.
In came the little girl in red.
She stopped. She stared. And then she said,

'*What great big ears you have, Grandma.*'
'*All the better to hear you with,*' the Wolf replied.
'*What great big eyes you have, Grandma,*'
  said Little Red Riding Hood.
'*All the better to see you with,*' the Wolf replied.

He sat there watching her and smiled.
He thought, I'm going to eat this child.
Compared with her old Grandmamma
She's going to taste like caviare.

Then Little Red Riding Hood said, '*But Grandma,
what a lovely great big furry coat you have on.*'

'That's wrong!' cried Wolf. 'Have you forgot
'To tell me what BIG TEETH I've got?
'Ah well, no matter what you say,
'I'm going to eat you anyway.'
The small girl smiles. One eyelid flickers.
She whips a pistol from her knickers.
She aims it at the creature's head
And *bang bang bang*, she shoots him dead.
A few weeks later, in the wood,
I came across Miss Riding Hood.
But what a change! No cloak of red,
No silly hood upon her head.
She said, 'Hello, and do please note
'My lovely furry WOLFSKIN COAT.'

ROALD DAHL

The African Lion

To meet a bad lad on the African waste
Is a thing that a lion enjoys;
But he rightly and strongly objects to the taste
Of good and uneatable boys.

When he bites off a piece of a boy of that sort
He spits it right out of his mouth,
And retires with a loud and dissatisfied snort
To the east, or the west, or the south.

So lads of good habits, on coming across
A lion, need feel no alarm,
For they know they are sure to escape with the loss
Of a leg, or a head, or an arm.

A. E. HOUSMAN

Earth, Earth, Under My Shoe

A Child's Song

Earth, earth, under my shoe,
you will swallow me whole.
I know you, earth,
you've a quicksand soul.

Sky, sky, over my hat,
you will fall on my head.
I know what you're up to, sky,
you'll flatten me dead.

Sea, sea, inside my socks,
you will drink me in.
I know not to trust you, sea,
you've a shark's grin.

Wind, wind, under my coat,
you will snuff me out.
I know your game, wind,
your hand's at my throat.

World, world, outside my room,
you will close your eye
till everything's dark and black
as the day I'll die.

CAROL ANN DUFFY

All Day Saturday

Let it sleet on Sunday,
Monday let it snow,
Let the mist on Tuesday
From the salt-sea flow.
Let it hail on Wednesday,
Thursday let it rain,
Let the wind on Friday
Blow a hurricane,
But Saturday, Saturday
Break fair and fine
And all day Saturday
Let the sun shine.

CHARLES CAUSLEY

Whether

Whether the weather be fine
Or whether the weather be not
Whether the weather be cold
Or whether the weather be hot—
We'll weather the weather
Whatever the weather
Whether we like it or not!

ANON.

What Is the Sun?

the Sun is an orange dinghy
  sailing across a calm sea

it is a gold coin
  dropped down a drain in heaven

the Sun is a yellow beach ball
  kicked high into the summer sky

it is a red thumb-print
  on a sheet of pale blue paper

the Sun is a milk bottle's golden top
  floating in a puddle

WES MAGEE

One Morning

One morning
—this morning—
the sound of the world
curled in through my window,
the sound of the world.

'Come follow,
go follow,'
the sound of the world
called in through my window,
the sound of the world.

And shall I
go follow
the sound of the world
that curled in and called me
this morning,
one morning?

NANCY CHAMBERS

Whispering Leaves

I am wondering
what it is
the leaves are whispering to me.
Which language they speak.
It doesn't seem funny
but it might be.
It takes years
getting leaf ears
only there aren't
many quiet days
to sit out and learn
leaf talk.
Leaves, I'm listening.

JULIE O'CALLAGHAN

The Trees

The trees are coming into leaf
Like something almost being said;
The recent buds relax and spread,
Their greenness is a kind of grief.

Is it that they are born again
And we grow old? No, they die too.
Their yearly trick of looking new
Is written down in rings of grain.

Yet still the unresting castles thresh
In fullgrown thickness every May.
Last year is dead, they seem to say,
Begin afresh, afresh, afresh.

PHILIP LARKIN

Seeds

The seeds I sowed—
For weeks unseen—
Have pushed up pygmy
Shoots of green;
So frail you'd think
The tiniest stone
Would never let
A glimpse be shown.
But no; a pebble
Near them lies,
At least a cherry-stone
In size,
Which that mere sprout
Has heaved away,
To bask in sunshine,
See the day.

WALTER DE LA MARE

i thank You God

i thank You God for most this amazing
day:for the leaping greenly spirits of trees
and a blue true dream of sky;and for everything
which is natural which is infinite which is yes

(i who have died am alive again today,
and this is the sun's birthday;this is the birth
day of life and of love and wings:and of the gay
great happening illimitably earth)

how should tasting touching hearing seeing
breathing any—lifted from the no
of all nothing—human merely being
doubt unimaginable You?

(now the ears of my ears awake and
now the eyes of my eyes are opened)

E. E. CUMMINGS

There Will Come Soft Rains

There will come soft rains and the smell of the ground,
And swallows circling with their shimmering sound;

And frogs in the pools singing at night,
And wild plum-trees in tremulous white;

Robins will wear their feathery fire
Whistling their whims on a low fence-wire;

And not one will know of the war, not one
Will care at last when it is done.

Not one would mind, neither bird nor tree
If mankind perished utterly;

And Spring herself, when she woke at dawn,
Would scarcely know that we were gone.

SARA TEASDALE

I Am the Rain

I am the rain
I like to play games
like sometimes
        I pretend
I'm going
        to fall
Man that's the time
I don't come at all

Like sometimes
I get these laughing stitches
up my sides
        rushing people in
and out
        with the clothesline
I just love drip
        dropping
down collars
        and spines
Maybe it's a shame
but it's the only way
I get some fame

GRACE NICHOLS

Summer Goes

Summer goes, summer goes
Like the sand between my toes
When the waves go out.
That's how summer pulls away,
Leaves me standing here today,
Waiting for the school bus.

Summer brought, summer brought
All the frogs that I have caught,
Frogging at the pond,
Hot dogs, flowers, shells and rocks,
Postcards in my postcard box—
Places far away.

Summer took, summer took
All the lessons in my book,
Blew them far away.
I forgot the things I knew—
Arithmetic and spelling too,
Never thought about them.

Summer's gone, summer's gone—
Fall and winter coming on,
Frosty in the morning.
Here's the school bus right on time.
I'm not really sad that I'm
Going back to school.

RUSSELL HOBAN

The Pelting Rain

Poor Johnny
he's lost it again
he's out trying to find it
in the pelting rain

the wild woods are thrashing
the weather's insane
trees double over

jays scream for shelter
the lamppost flashes
signals for rescue

and Johnny'd better
skid helter-skelter
for safe haven

but he's gone again
poor Johnny
looking for sunshine
in the pelting rain.

HELEN DUNMORE

The Day That Summer Died

From all around the mourners came
 The day that Summer died,
From hill and valley, field and wood
 And lake and mountainside.

They did not come in funeral black
 But every mourner chose
Gorgeous colours or soft shades
 Of russet, yellow, rose.

Horse chestnut, oak and sycamore
 Wore robes of gold and red;
The rowan sported scarlet beads;
 No bitter tears were shed;

Although at dusk the mourners heard,
 As a small wind softly sighed,
A touch of sadness in the air
 The day that Summer died.

VERNON SCANNELL

Something Told the Wild Geese

Something told the wild geese
It was time to go,
Though the fields lay golden
Something whispered, 'Snow!'
Leaves were green and stirring,
Berries lustre-glossed,
But beneath warm feathers
Something cautioned, 'Frost!'

All the sagging orchards
Steamed with amber spice,
But each wild beast stiffened
At remembered ice.
Something told the wild geese
It was time to fly—
Summer sun was on their wings,
Winter in their cry.

RACHEL FIELD

From the Winter Wind

From the winter wind
a cold fly
came to our window
where we had frozen our noses
and warmed his feet on the glass.

MICHAEL ROSEN

Trees

The trees are shrieking
Their hands thrust up in fright
Like an army of bone-men on the hill
Stopped in their tracks and turned to skin and stone.

BERLIE DOHERTY

On Bonfire Night

On bonfire night
seeing a wigwam of planks
being burnt
and concerned
about its future
the nearby fence
looks tense

JOHN HEGLEY

The Garden Year

January brings the snow,
Makes our feet and fingers glow.

February brings the rain,
Thaws the frozen lake again.

March brings breezes, loud and shrill,
To stir the dancing daffodil.

April brings the primrose sweet,
Scatters daisies at our feet.

May brings flocks of pretty lambs
Skipping by their fleecy dams.

June brings tulips, lilies, roses,
Fills the children's hands with posies.

Hot July brings cooling showers,
Apricots, and gillyflowers.

August brings the sheaves of corn,
Then the harvest home is borne.

Warm September brings the fruit;
Sportsmen then begin to shoot.

Fresh October brings the pheasant;
Then to gather nuts is pleasant.

Dull November brings the blast;
Then the leaves are whirling fast.

Chill December brings the sleet,
Blazing fire, and Christmas treat.

SARA COLERIDGE

Windows

When you look before you go
Outside in the rain or snow,
It looks colder, it looks wetter
Through the window. It is better
When you're outside in it.

When you're out and it's still light
Even though it's almost night
And your mother at the door
Calls you in, there is no more
Daylight in the window
When you're inside looking out.

Russell Hoban

It's Only the Storm

'What's that creature that rattles the roof?'
'Hush, it's only the storm.'

'What's blowing the tiles and the branches off?'
'Hush, it's only the storm.'

'What's riding the sky like a wild white horse,
Flashing its teeth and stamping its hooves?'

'Hush, my dear, it's only the storm,
Racing the darkness till it catches the dawn.
Hush, my dear, it's only the storm,
When you wake in the morning, it will be gone.'

DAVID GREYGOOSE

An Ordinary Day

I took my mind a walk
Or my mind took me a walk—
Whichever was the truth of it.

The light glittered on the water
Or the water glittered in the light.
Cormorants stood on a tidal rock

With their wings spread out,
Stopping no traffic. Various ducks
Shilly-shallied here and there

On the shilly-shallying water.
An occasional gull yelped. Small flowers
Were doing their level best

To bring to their kerb bees like
Aerial charabancs. Long weeds in the clear
Water did Eastern dances, unregarded

By shoals of darning needles. A cow
Started a moo but thought
Better of it . . . And my feet took me home

And my mind observed to me,
Or I to it, how ordinary
Extraordinary things are or

How extraordinary ordinary
Things are, like the nature of the mind
And the process of observing.

NORMAN MACCAIG

Little Boy Blue

When young, I walked the winter fields
collecting wool that snagged on fences,
yellowing strands from backs of sheep
that huddled silly into corners.

Now shreds of plastic flag the trees
and hedges where I wander.
I look and look but never spot
the farmer's blue and plastic flock.

JOHN CORBEN

maggie and milly and molly and may

maggie and milly and molly and may
went down to the beach(to play one day)

and maggie discovered a shell that sang
so sweetly she couldn't remember her troubles,and

milly befriended a stranded star
whose rays five languid fingers were;

and molly was chased by a horrible thing
which raced sideways while blowing bubbles:and

may came home with a smooth round stone
as small as a world and as large as alone.

For whatever we lose(like a you or a me)
it's always ourselves we find in the sea

E .E. CUMMINGS

Sea-Fever

I must down to the seas again, to the lonely sea and the sky,
And all I ask is a tall ship and a star to steer her by,
And the wheel's kick and the wind's song and the white sail's
shaking,
And a grey mist on the sea's face, and a grey dawn breaking.

I must down to the seas again, for the call of the running tide
Is a wild call and a clear call that may not be denied;
And all I ask is a windy day with the white clouds flying,
And the flung spray and the blown spume, and the sea-gulls
crying.

I must down to the seas again, to the vagrant gypsy life,
To the gull's way and the whale's way where the wind's like a
whetted knife;
And all I ask is a merry yarn from a laughing fellow-rover
And quiet sleep and a sweet dream when the long trick's over.

JOHN MASEFIELD

Stones by the Sea

Smooth and flat, grey, brown and white,
Winter and summer, noon and night,
Tumbling together for a thousand ages,
We ought to be wiser than Eastern sages.
But no doubt we stones are foolish as most,
So we don't say much on our stretch of coast.
Quiet and peaceful we mainly sit,
And when storms come up we grumble a bit.

JAMES REEVES

Walking Across the Atlantic

I wait for the holiday crowd to clear the beach
before stepping onto the first wave.

Soon I am walking across the Atlantic
thinking about Spain,
checking for whales, waterspouts.

I feel the water holding up my shifting weight.
Tonight I will sleep on its rocking surface.

But for now I try to imagine what
this must look like to the fish below,
the bottoms of my feet appearing, disappearing.

BILLY COLLINS

Tell Me, Tell Me, Sarah Jane

Tell me, tell me, Sarah Jane,
   Tell me, dearest daughter,
Why are you holding in your hand
   A thimbleful of water?
Why do you hold it to your eye
   And gaze both late and soon
From early morning light until
   The rising of the moon?

Mother, I hear the mermaids cry,
   I hear the mermen sing,
And I can see the sailing-ships
   All made of sticks and string.
And I can see the jumping fish,
   The whales that fall and rise
And swim about the waterspout
   That swarms up to the skies.

Tell me, tell me, Sarah Jane,
  Tell your darling mother,
Why do you walk beside the tide
  As though you loved none other?
Why do you listen to a shell
  And watch the billows curl,
And throw away your diamond ring
  And wear instead the pearl?

Mother, I hear the water
  Beneath the headland pinned,
And I can see the sea-gull
  Sliding down the wind.
I taste the salt upon my tongue
  As sweet as sweet can be.

Tell me, my dear, whose voice you hear?

It is the sea, the sea.

CHARLES CAUSLEY

They Call to One Another

They call to one another
    in the prisons of the sea
the mermen and mermaidens
    bound under lock and key
down in the green and salty dens
    and dungeons of the sea,
lying about in chains but
    dying to be free:
and this is why shortsighted men
    believe them not to be
for down to their dark dungeons it
    is very hard to see.

But sometimes morning fishermen
    drag up in the net
bits of bright glass or the silver comb
    of an old vanity set
or a letter rather hard to read
    because it is still wet
sent to remind us never, never
    never to forget
the mermen and mermaidens
    in the prisons of the sea
who call to one another
    when the stars of morning rise
and the stars of evening set
    for I have heard them calling
and I can hear them, yet.

GEORGE BARKER

The Forsaken Merman

Come, dear children, let us away;
Down and away below!
Now my brothers call from the bay,
Now the great winds shoreward blow,
Now the salt tides seaward flow;
Now the wild white horses play,
Champ and chafe and toss in the spray.
Children dear, let us away!
This way, this way!

Call her once before you go—
Call once yet!
In a voice that she will know:
'Margaret! Margaret!'
Children's voices should be dear
(Call once more) to a mother's ear;
Children's voices, wild with pain—
Surely she will come again!
Call her once and come away;
This way, this way!
'Mother dear, we cannot stay!
The wild white horses foam and fret.'
Margaret! Margaret!

Come, dear children, come away down;
Call no more!
One last look at the white-wall'd town,
And the little grey church on the windy shore;
Then come down!
She will not come though you call all day;
Come away, come away!

Children dear, was it yesterday
We heard the sweet bells over the bay?
In the caverns where we lay,
Through the surf and through the swell,
The far-off sound of a silver bell?

Sand-strewn caverns, cool and deep,
Where the winds are all asleep;
Where the spent lights quiver and gleam,
Where the salt weed sways in the stream,
Where the sea-beasts, ranged all round,
Feed in the ooze of their pasture-ground;
Where the sea-snakes coil and twine,
Dry their mail and bask in the brine;
Where great whales come sailing by,
Sail and sail, with unshut eye,
Round the world for ever and aye?
When did music come this way?
Children dear, was it yesterday?

Children dear, was it yesterday
(Call yet once) that she went away?
Once she sate with you and me,
On a red gold throne in the heart of the sea,
And the youngest sate on her knee.
She comb'd its bright hair, and she tended it well,
When down swung the sound of a far-off bell.
She sigh'd, she look'd up through the clear green sea;
She said: 'I must go, for my kinsfolk pray
In the little grey church on the shore to-day.
'Twill be Easter-time in the world—ah me!
And I lose my poor soul, Merman! here with thee.'

I said: 'Go up, dear heart, through the waves;
Say thy prayer, and come back to the kind sea-caves!'
She smiled, she went up through the surf in the bay.
Children dear, was it yesterday?

Children dear, were we long alone?
'The sea grows stormy, the little ones moan;
Long prayers,' I said, 'in the world they say;
Come!' I said; and we rose through the surf in the bay.
We went up the beach, by the sandy down
Where the sea-stocks bloom, to the white-wall'd town;
Through the narrow paved streets, where all was still,
To the little grey church on the windy hill.
From the church came a murmur of folk at their prayers,
But we stood without in the cold blowing airs.
We climb'd on the graves, on the stones worn with rains,
And we gazed up the aisle through the small leaded panes.
She sate by the pillar; we saw her clear:
'Margaret, hist! come quick, we are here!
Dear heart,' I said, 'we are long alone;
The sea grows stormy, the little ones moan.'
But, ah, she gave me never a look,
For her eyes were seal'd to the holy book!
Loud prays the priest; shut stands the door.
Come away, children, call no more!
Come away, come down, call no more!

Down, down, down!
Down to the depths of the sea!
She sits at her wheel in the humming town,
Singing most joyfully.
Hark what she sings: 'O joy, O joy,
For the humming street, and the child with its toy!

For the priest, and the bell, and the holy well;
For the wheel where I spun,
And the blessed light of the sun!'
And so she sings her fill,
Singing most joyfully,
Till the spindle drops from her hand,
And the whizzing wheel stands still.
She steals to the window, and looks at the sand,
And over the sand at the sea;
And her eyes are set in a stare;
And anon there breaks a sigh,
And anon there drops a tear,
From a sorrow-clouded eye,
And a heart sorrow-laden,
A long, long sigh;
For the cold strange eyes of a little Mermaiden
And the gleam of her golden hair.

Come, children, come down!
The hoarse wind blows coldly;
Lights shine in the town.
She will start from her slumber
When gusts shake the door;
She will hear the winds howling,
Will hear the waves roar.
We shall see, while above us
The waves roar and whirl,
A ceiling of amber,
A pavement of pearl.

Singing: 'Here came a mortal,
But faithless was she!
And alone dwell for ever
The kings of the sea.'

But, children, at midnight,
When soft the winds blow,
When clear falls the moonlight,
When spring-tides are low;
When sweet airs come seaward
From heaths starr'd with broom,
And high rocks throw mildly
On the blanch'd sands a gloom;
Up the still, glistening beaches,
Up the creeks we will hie,
Over banks of bright seaweed
The ebb-tide leaves dry.
We will gaze, from the sand-hills,
At the white, sleeping town;
At the church on the hill-side—
And then come back down.
Singing: 'There dwells a loved one,
But cruel is she!
She left lonely for ever
The kings of the sea.'

MATTHEW ARNOLD

Grim and Gloomy

Oh, grim and gloomy,
So grim and gloomy
Are the caves beneath the sea.
Oh, rare but roomy
And bare and boomy,
Those salt sea caverns be.

Oh, slim and slimy
Or grey and grimy
Are the animals of the sea.
Salt and oozy
And safe and snoozy
The caves where those animals be.

Hark to the shuffling,
Huge and snuffling,
Ravenous, cavernous, great sea-beasts!
But fair and fabulous,
Tintinnabulous,
Gay and fabulous are their feasts.

Ah, but the queen of the sea,
The querulous, perilous sea!
How the curls of her tresses
The pearls on her dresses,
Sway and swirl in the waves,
How cosy and dozy,
How sweet ring-a-rosy
Her bower in the deep-sea caves!

Oh, rare but roomy
And bare and boomy
Those caverns under the sea,
And grave and grandiose,
Safe and sandiose
The dens of her denizens be.

JAMES REEVES

Horses on the Camargue

In the grey wastes of dread,
The haunt of shattered gulls where nothing moves
But in a shroud of silence like the dead,
I heard a sudden harmony of hooves,
And, turning, saw afar
A hundred snowy horses unconfined,
The silver runaways of Neptune's car
Racing, spray curled, like waves before the wind.
Sons of the Mistral, fleet
As him with whose strong gusts they love to flee,
Who shod the flying thunders on their feet
And plumed them with the snortings of the sea;
Theirs is no earthly breed
Who only haunt the verges of the earth
And only on the sea's salt herbage feed—
Surely the great white breakers gave them birth.
For when for years a slave,
A horse of the Camargue, in alien lands,
Should catch some far-off fragrance of the wave
Carried far inland from his native sands,
Many have told the tale
Of how in fury, foaming at the rein,
He hurls his rider; and with lifted tail,
With coal-red eyes and cataracting mane,
Heading his course for home,
Though sixty foreign leagues before him sweep,
Will never rest until he breathes the foam
And hears the native thunder of the deep.
But when the great gusts rise
And lash their anger on these arid coasts,

When the scared gulls career with mournful cries
And whirl across the waste like driven ghosts:
When hail and fire converge,
The only souls to which they strike no pain
Are the white-crested fillies of the surge
And the white horses of the windy plain.
Then in their strength and pride
The stallions of the wilderness rejoice;
They feel their Master's trident in their side,
And high and shrill they answer to his voice.
With white tails smoking free,
Long streaming manes, and arching necks, they show
Their kinship to their sisters of the sea—
And forward hurl their thunderbolts of snow.
Still out of hardship bred,
Spirits of power and beauty and delight
Have ever on such frugal pastures fed
And loved to course with tempests through the night.

ROY CAMPBELL

Casabianca

The boy stood on the burning deck
  Whence all but he had fled;
The flame that lit the battle's wreck
  Shone round him o'er the dead.

The flames rolled on. He would not go
  Without his father's word;
That father faint in death below,
  His voice no longer heard.

He called aloud: 'Say, father, say
  If yet my task is done!'
He knew not that the chieftain lay
  Unconscious of his son.

'Speak, father!' once again he cried,
  'If I may yet be gone!'
And but the booming shots replied,
  And fast the flames rolled on.

Upon his brow he felt their breath,
  And in his waving hair,
And looked from that lone post of death
  In still yet brave despair;

And shouted but once more aloud,
  'My father! must I stay?'
While o'er him fast through sail and shroud,
  The wreathing fires made way.

They wrapt the ship in splendour wild,
  They caught the flag on high,
And streamed above the gallant child
  Like banners in the sky.

Then came a burst of thunder-sound—
  The boy—oh! where was he?
Ask of the winds that far around
  With fragments strewed the sea,

With mast, and helm, and pennon fair,
  That well had borne their part.
But the noblest thing that perished there
  Was that young faithful heart.

Felicia Hemans

Mary Celeste

Only the wind sings
in the riggings,
the hull creaks a lullaby;
a sail lifts gently
like a message
pinned to a vacant sky.
The wheel turns
over bare decks,
shirts flap on a line;
only the song of the lapping waves
beats steady time . . .

First mate,
off-duty from
the long dawn watch, begins
a letter to his wife, daydreams
of home.

The Captain's wife is late;
the child did not sleep
and breakfast has passed . . .
She, too, is missing home;
sits down at last to eat,
but can't quite force
the porridge down.
She swallows hard,
slices the top from her egg.

The second mate
is happy.
A four-hour sleep,
full stomach
and a quiet sea
are all he craves.
He has all three.

Shirts washed and hung, beds
made below, decks done, the boy
stitches a torn sail.

The Captain
has a good ear for a tune;
played his child to sleep
on the ship's organ,
Now, music left,
he checks his compass,
lightly tips the wheel,
hopes for a westerly.
Clear sky, a friendly sea,
fair winds for Italy.

The child now sleeps, at last,
head firmly pressed into her pillow
in a deep sea-dream.

Then why are the gulls wheeling
like vultures in the sky?
Why was the child snatched
from her sleep? What drew
the Captain's cry?

Only the wind replies
in the rigging,
and the hull creaks and sighs;
a sail spells out its message
over silent skies.
The wheel still turns
over bare decks,
shirts blow on the line;
the siren-song of lapping waves
still echoes over time.

JUDITH NICHOLLS

from The Ancient Mariner

And now the STORM-BLAST came, and he
Was tyrannous and strong:
He struck with his o'ertaking wings,
And chased us south along.

With sloping masts and dipping prow,
As who pursued with yell and blow
Still treads the shadow of his foe,
And forward bends his head,
The ship drove fast, loud roared the blast,
And southward aye we fled.

And now there came both mist and snow,
And it grew wondrous cold:
And ice, mast-high, came floating by,
As green as emerald.

And through the drifts the snowy clifts
Did send a dismal sheen:
Nor shapes of men nor beasts we ken—
The ice was all between.

The ice was here, the ice was there,
The ice was all around:
It cracked and growled, and roared and howled,
Like noises in a swound!

✦ ✦ ✦

The fair breeze blew, the white foam flew,
The furrow followed free;
We were the first that ever burst
Into that silent sea.

Down dropt the breeze, the sails dropt down,
'Twas sad as sad could be;
And we did speak only to break
The silence of the sea!

All in a hot and copper sky,
The bloody Sun, at noon,
Right up above the mast did stand,
No bigger than the Moon.

Day after day, day after day,
We stuck, nor breath nor motion;
As idle as a painted ship
Upon a painted ocean.

Water, water, every where,
And all the boards did shrink;
Water, water, every where,
Nor any drop to drink.

The very deep did rot: O Christ!
That ever this should be!
Yea, slimy things did crawl with legs
Upon the slimy sea.

About, about, in reel and rout
The death-fires danced at night;
The water, like a witch's oils,
Burnt green, and blue and white.

SAMUEL TAYLOR COLERIDGE

Lake Superior

I am Lake Superior
Cold and grey.
I have no superior;
All other lakes
Haven't got what it takes;
All are inferior.
I am Lake Superior
Cold and grey.
I am so cold
That because I chill them
The girls of Fort William
Can't swim in me.
I am so deep
That when people drown in me
Their relatives weep
For they'll never find them.
In me swims the fearsome
Great big sturgeon.
My shores are made of iron
Lined with tough, wizened trees.
No knife of a surgeon
Is sharper than these
Waves of mine
That glitter and shine
In the light of the Moon, my mother
In the light of the Sun, my grandmother.

JAMES REANEY

Jonah and the Whale

Well, to start with
It was dark
So dark
You couldn't see
Your hand in front of your face;
And huge
Huge as an acre of farm-land.
How do I know?
Well, I paced it out
Length and breadth
That's how.
And if you was to shout
You'd hear your own voice resound,
Bouncing along the ridges of its stomach,
Like when you call out
Under a bridge
Or in an empty hall.
Hear anything?
No not much.
Only the normal
Kind of sounds
You'd expect to hear
Inside a whale's stomach;
The sea swishing far away,
Food gurgling, the wind
And suchlike sounds;
Then there was me screaming for help,
But who'd be likely to hear,
Us being miles from
Any shipping lines

And anyway
Supposing someone did hear,
Who'd think of looking inside a whale?
That's not the sort of thing
That people do.
Smell? I'll say there was a smell.
And cold. The wind blew in
Something terrible from the South
Each time he opened his mouth
Or took a swallow of some tit bit.
The only way I found
To keep alive at all
Was to wrap my arms
Tight around myself
And race from wall to wall.
Damp? You can say that again;
When the ocean came sluicing in
I had to climb his ribs
To save myself from drowning.
Fibs? You think I'm telling you fibs.
I haven't told the half of it, brother.
I'm only giving a modest account
Of what these two eyes have seen
And that's the truth on it.
Here, one thing I'll say
Before I'm done—
Catch me eating fish
From now on.

GARETH OWEN

Song of the Open Road

I think that I shall never see
A billboard lovely as a tree.
Indeed, unless the billboards fall
I'll never see a tree at all.

OGDEN NASH

Between Walls

the back wings
of the

hospital where
nothing

will grow lie
cinders

in which shine
the broken

pieces of a green
bottle

WILLIAM CARLOS WILLIAMS

Motorway

Motorway—motorway—motorway,
Never stay—never stay—never stay,
Broad bridge ribbon overrides us,
Giant-strides us,
Manmade dinosaurus, dwarfs us.

Motor-metal fleas fly by,
Whining car horns grow and die,
Skim the giant's broad black back,
White line,
Sign post,
Motor track.

Listen in your sleep, dream deep,
Hear him stamp his giant feet,
Beating, beating, street on street,
Motorway—motorway—motorway.

MARIAN LINES

A Speck Speaks

About ten million years ago
I was a speck of rock in a vast black rock.
My address was:
    Vast Black Rock,
    Near Italy,
    Twelve Metres Under
The Mediterranean Sea.

The other specks and I
Formed an impressive edifice—
Bulbously curving at the base
With rounded caves
And fun tunnels for the fish,
Romantically jagged at the top.

Life, for us specks, was uneventful—
One for all, welded together
In the cool, salty wet.
What more could specks
Expect?

Each year a few of us were lost,
Scrubbed from the edges of the rock
By the washerwoman waters
Which smoothed our base, whittled our cornices
And sharpened our pinnacles.
As the rock slowly shed skin-thin layers
It was my turn to be exposed
Among the packed grit of its surface,
(Near the tip of the fifty-ninth spire
From the end of the eastern outcrop).

One day, it was a Wednesday I remember,
A scampi flicked me off my perch
Near the vast black rock's peak
And I was scurried down
Long corridors of currents
Until a wave caught me in its mouth
And spat me out on—
What?

A drying stretch
Of yellow, white, black, red and transparent specks,
Billions of particles,
Loosely organized in bumps and dips;
Quite unlike the tight hard group
Which I belonged to in the good old rock.
Heat banged down on us all day long.
Us? I turned to the speck next to me,
A lumpish red fellow who'd been washed off a brick.

'I'm new here,' I confessed,
'What are we supposed to be?'
He bellowed back—
(But the bellow of a speck
Is less than the whispering of ants)—
'We're grains now, grains of sand,
And this society is called Beach.'

'Beach?' I said. 'What are we grains supposed to do?'
'Just stray around, lie loose,
Go with the wind, go with the sea
And sink down when you're trodden on.'

'Don't know if I can manage that.
Used to belong to the Vast Black Rock
And we all stuck together.'

'Give Beach a try,' said the red grain.
Well, there was no alternative.

Many eras later
I was just beginning to feel
Part of Beach, that slow-drifting,
Slow-shifting, casual community,
When I was shovelled up
With a ton of fellow grains,
Hoisted into a lorry, shaken down a road,
Washed, sifted and poured in a machine
Hotter than the sunshine.

When they poured me out, life had changed again.
My mates and I swam in a molten river
Down into a mould.
White-hot we were, then red, then
Suddenly cold
And we found ourselves merged
Into a tall, circular tower,
Wide at the bottom, narrow at the top.
What's more, we'd all turned green as sea-weed.
Transparent green.
We had become—a wine bottle.

In a few flashes of time
We'd been filled with wine,
Stoppered, labelled, bumped to a shop,
Stood in a window, sold, refrigerated,
Drained by English tourists,
Transmogrified into a lampstand,
Smashed by a four-year-old called Tarquin,
Swept up, chucked in the garbage, hauled away,
Dumped and bulldozed into the sea.

Now the underwater years sandpaper away
My shield-shaped fragment of bottle.
So one day I shall be a single grain again,
A single grain of green, transparent glass.

When that day comes
I will transmit a sub-aquatic call
To all green specks of glass
Proposing that we form
A Vast Green Rock of Glass
Near Italy
Twelve Metres Under
The Mediterranean Sea.

Should be pretty spectacular
In about ten million years.

All being well.

ADRIAN MITCHELL

Natural Anthem

God save our gracious green
Long live our glorious scene
God save our green.

Dis ting is serious
Do it for all of us
Save our asparagus,
God save
Our
Green.

BENJAMIN ZEPHANIAH

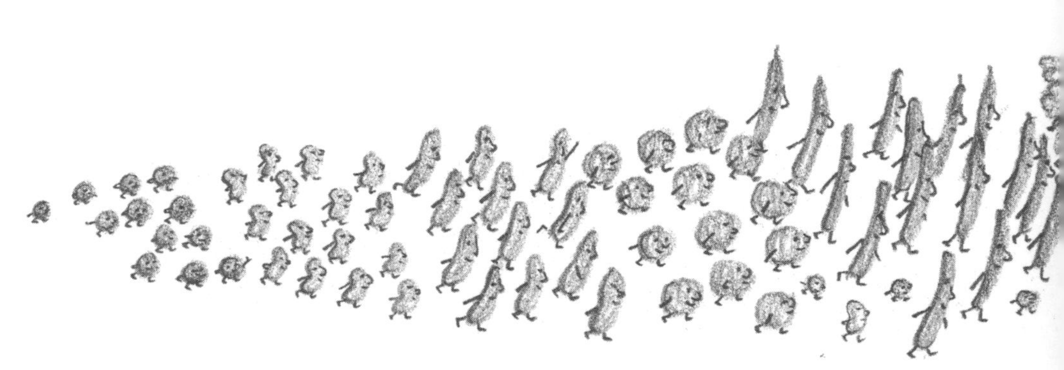

Solidarity

An army of militant greens
In bio-degradable genes
Shout 'Give peas a chance
An lettuce all dance
In unity wid butter beans'.

BENJAMIN ZEPHANIAH

Wanted: World-Sitter

WANTED: sitter
to care for this
elderly world:
to look after
all its many needs,

to keep it going
until its last day,
the extinction
of all its life.
You must stop it

becoming too warm
as this just leads
to storms and floods
of tears and to
so much damage.

You will not be
liked. All of us
comfortable
people will hate
all that you say.

SUSANNA DALTON

I Am the Song

I Am the Song

I am the song that sings the bird.
I am the leaf that grows the land.
I am the tide that moves the moon.
I am the stream that halts the sand.
I am the cloud that drives the storm.
I am the earth that lights the sun.
I am the fire that strikes the stone.
I am the clay that shapes the hand.
I am the word that speaks the man.

CHARLES CAUSLEY

Looking at Pictures

I would like a walled garden with flowers hanging
In cascades down white-washed pillars in the sun.
I would like hounds on leashes.
I would like not to be me.

But if I lived in a past age and had another body
Perhaps I would look *out* of this picture book and think
'I would like a world where babies did not die, where
Children were not whipped and where people believed what
    was true.
I would like not to be "important" and afraid; to play in the street
And laugh without hiding bad teeth and have clean hair
And go in for my tea when someone called, instead of ordering it.
Oh beautiful tough and lucky little children
I would like to be *you*.'

JENNY JOSEPH

The Secret Sits

We dance round in a ring and suppose,
But the Secret sits in the middle and knows.

ROBERT FROST

What is Christmas?

Christmas is
  a lighted island
In the sea
  of winter darkness.

Christmas is
  the reindeer clatter
On the roof of
  the rustling house.

Christmas is
  the spiced kitchen
Spreading through
  the waiting days.

Christmas is
  the tongue teased
And the tummy
  truly tested.

Christmas is
  the warm hug
That wraps me in
  my family's love.

MICHAEL RICHARDS

Divali

Winter stalks us
like a leopard in the mountains
scenting prey.

It grows dark,
bare trees stick black bars
across the moon's silver eye.

I will light my lamp for you
Lakshmi,
drive away the darkness.

Welcome you into my home
Lakshmi,
beckon you from every window

With light that blazes
out like flames
across the sombre sky.

Certain houses
crouch in shadow, do not hear
your gentle voice.

Will not feel
your gentle heartbeat
bring prosperity and fortune.

Darkness hunts them
like a leopard in the mountains
stalking prey.

DAVID HARMER

Prayer to Laughter

O Laughter
giver of relaxed mouths

you who rule our belly with tickles
you who come when not called
you who can embarrass us at times

send us stitches in our sides
shake us till the water reaches our eyes
buckle our knees till we cannot stand

we whose faces are grim and shattered
we whose hearts are no longer hearty
O Laughter we beg you

crack us up
crack us up

JOHN AGARD

from The Great Lover

These I have loved:
    White plates and cups, clean-gleaming,
Ringed with blue lines; and feathery, faery dust;
Wet roofs, beneath the lamp-light; the strong crust
Of friendly bread; and many-tasting food;
Rainbows; and the blue bitter smoke of wood;
And radiant raindrops couching in cool flowers;
And flowers themselves, that sway through sunny hours,
Dreaming of moths that drink them under the moon;
Then, the cool kindliness of sheets, that soon
Smooth away trouble; and the rough male kiss
Of blankets; grainy wood; live hair that is
Shining and free; blue-massing clouds; the keen
Unpassioned beauty of a great machine;
The benison of hot water; furs to touch;
The good smell of old clothes; and others such—
The comfortable smell of friendly fingers,
Hair's fragrance, and the musty reek that lingers
About dead leaves and last year's ferns . . .

RUPERT BROOKE

Eternity

He who binds to himself a joy
Does the winged life destroy;
But he who kisses the joy as it flies
Lives in eternity's sun rise.

WILLIAM BLAKE

To Everything There Is a Season

To everything there is a season
and a time to every purpose under the heaven:

A time to be born, and a time to die;
a time to plant and a time to pluck up that which is planted;

A time to kill, and a time to heal;
a time to break down, and a time to build up;

A time to weep, and a time to laugh;
a time to mourn, and a time to dance;

A time to cast away stones, and a time to gather stones
    together;
a time to embrace, and a time to refrain from embracing;

A time to get, and a time to lose;
a time to keep, and a time to cast away;

A time to rend, and a time to sew;
a time to keep silence, and a time to speak;

A time to love, and a time to hate;
a time of war, and a time of peace.

ECCLESIASTES 3: 1-8
THE BIBLE: KING JAMES VERSION

Good Hope

I believe
There is enough food
On this planet
For everyone.

I believe
That it is possible
For all people
To live in peace.

I believe
We can live
Without guns,
I believe everyone
Is important.

I believe there are good Christians
And good Muslims,
Good Jews
And good not sures,
I believe
There is good in everyone
I believe in people.

If I did not believe
I would stop writing.

I know
Every day
Children cry for water,
And every day
Racists attack,

Still every day
Children play
With no care for colour.

So I believe **there is hope**
And I hope
That there are many believers
Believing
There is hope,
That is what I hope,
And this is what I believe,
I believe in you,
Believe me.

BENJAMIN ZEPHANIAH

Index of titles and first lines

Index of poets

Acknowledgements

John Agard: 'Don't Call Alligator Long-Mouth Till You Cross River' copyright © 1986 by John Agard; 'My Telly' copyright © 1983 by John Agard; 'Prayer to Laughter' copyright © 1986 by John Agard, all reproduced by kind permission of John Agard c/o Caroline Sheldon Literary Agency Limited. **Allan Ahlberg:** 'Who Knows?' from *Please Mrs Butler* (Kestrel, 1983), copyright © Allan Ahlberg, 1983, reproduced by permission of Penguin Books Limited; 'The Footballer's Love of the Ball' and 'Polite Children' from *Friendly Matches* (Viking, 2001), copyright © Allan Ahlberg, 2001, reproduced by permission of Penguin Books Limited. **W. H. Auden:** 'The Night Mail' from *Collected Poems* (Faber) © W. H. Auden, reprinted by permission of Faber and Faber Ltd. **George Barker:** 'They Call to One Another' from *To Aylsham Fair* (Faber, 1970) © George Barker, reprinted by permission of Faber and Faber Ltd. **Patricia Beer:** 'Abbey Tomb' from *Collected Poems* (Carcanet, 1988) by permission of Carcanet Press Limited. **Hilaire Belloc:** 'Matilda' and 'The Frog' from *Complete Verse* by Hilaire Belloc (copyright © The Estate of Hilaire Belloc 1970) is reproduced by permission of PFD (www.pfd.co.uk) on behalf of the Estate of Hilaire Belloc. **Gerard Benson:** 'Hlep!' and 'Lim' from *The Magnificent Callisto* and 'Evidence of Elephants' from *Evidence of Elephants* © Gerard Benson, reproduced by permission of the author. **Carmen Bernos de Gasztold (translated by Rumer Godden):** 'The Prayer of the Mouse' reproduced with permission of Curtis Brown Group Ltd, London on behalf of the Estate of Rumer Godden. Copyright © Rumer Godden 1965. **James Berry:** 'Dreaming Black Boy', 'Absent Player', and 'Playing a Dazzler' from *Playing a Dazzler* by James Berry (copyright © James Berry, 1995) are reproduced by kind permission of PFD (www.pfd.co.uk) on behalf of James Berry. **Valerie Bloom:** 'Chicken Poxed' and 'Why Is It?' © 2000 Valerie Bloom, from *Let Me Touch the Sky* published by Macmillan Children's Books, reprinted by permission of Valerie Bloom. **Gary Boswell:** 'Ducks Don't Shop in Sainsbury's' from *It's Brilliant* copyright © Gary Boswell, reproduced by permission of the author. **Alan Brownjohn:** 'We Are Going to See the Rabbit' © Alan Brownjohn. Alan Brownjohn's *Collected Poems* are published by Enitharmon Press. **Roy Campbell:** 'Horses on the Camargue' from *Adamstor* © Jonathan Ball Publishers through DALRO (Pty) Ltd, South Africa 2007. **Charles Causley:** 'As I Went Down the Cat-Walk', 'By St Thomas Water', 'All Day Saturday', 'I Am the Song', 'Stone in the Water', 'Good Morning, Mr Croco-doco-dile', '"Quack!" Said the Billy Goat' and 'Tell Me, Tell Me, Sarah Jane' all from *Collected Poems* (Macmillan) by permission of David Higham Associates. **Nancy Chambers:** 'One Morning' © 1981 Nancy Chambers from *Stir-About* by Nancy Chambers. Reproduced by permission of Walker Books Ltd, London SE11 5HJ. **Hugh Chesterman:** 'Noah and the Rabbit' © Hugh Chesterman, from *Noah's Ark* (OUP, 1983). **Leonard Clark:** 'Good Company' © Leonard Clark, from *Good Company* (Dobson Books). **Billy Collins:** 'On Turning Ten' and 'Walking Across the Atlantic' from *Sailing Around the Room* reprinted by permission of SLL/Sterling Lord Literistic Inc. Copyright © Billy Collins. **Wendy Cope:** 'The Uncertainty of the Poet' from *Serious Concerns* and 'Tich Miller' from *Making Cocoa for Kingsley Amis* © Wendy Cope, reprinted by permission of Faber and Faber Ltd. **John Corben:** 'Granny Smith: Best Before Feb 21' and 'Little Boy Blue' reprinted by permission of Michael Harrison. **Sue Cowling:** 'Looking Forward' from *What is a Kumquat* copyright © Sue Cowling, reprinted by permission of the author. **E. E. Cummings:** 'i thank You God for most this amazing' and 'maggie and milly and molly and may' are reprinted from COMPLETE POEMS 1904-1962, by E. E. Cummings, edited by George J. Firmage, by permission of W. W. Norton & Company. Copyright © 1991 by the Trustees for the E. E. Cummings Trust and George James Firmage. **Roald Dahl:** 'Little Red Riding Hood and the Wolf' from *Revolting Rhymes* (Jonathan Cape and Penguin Books Ltd) © Roald Dahl by permission of David Higham Associates Ltd. **Susanna Dalton:** 'Wanted: World-Sitter' reprinted by permission of Michael Harrison. **W. H. Davies:** 'Leisure' from *Complete Poems* (Cape) © W. H. Davies. **Walter de la Mare:** 'Tartary', 'The Listeners', and 'Seeds' reproduced by permission of The Society of Authors as the Literary Representative of Walter de la Mare. **Olive Dehn:** 'The Park' © Olive Dehn reproduced by permission of the author. **Peter Dixon:** 'Teabag' from *Grow Your Own Poems* and 'Nativity Play' from *The Tortoise Has a Mighty Roar* © Peter Dixon. Reproduced by permission of the author. **Berlie Doherty:** 'Playgrounds', 'Ghost in the Garden', and 'Trees' from *Walking on Air* (Hodder Children's Books) © Berlie Doherty. Reproduced by permission of David Higham Associates Ltd. **Carol Ann Duffy:** 'Secrets', 'Jamjar', and 'A Child's Song' from *The Good Child's Guide to Rock and Roll* (Faber) © Carol Ann Duffy, reprinted by permission of Faber and Faber Ltd. **Michael Dugan:** 'Nightening' © Michael Dugan, from *Flocks, Socks and Other Shocks*.**Helen Dunmore:** 'The Pelting Rain' from *Snollygoster* (Scholastic) © Helen Dunmore. Reproduced by permission of A. P. Watt Ltd on behalf of Helen Dunmore. **Richard Edwards:** 'When I Was Three' and 'Just My Luck' from *The Word Party*. Copyright © Richard Edwards. Reproduced by permission of the author. **T. S. Eliot:** 'The Song of the Jellicles' from *Old Possum's Book of Practical Cats* (Faber) © The Estate of T. S. Eliot, reprinted by permission of Faber and Faber Ltd. **U. A. Fanthorpe:** 'Children Imagining a Hospital' and 'Half-Past Two' from *Neck Verse* and 'Reindeer Report' from *Poems for Christmas*, all poems © U. A. Fanthorpe and reproduced by permission of Peterloo Poets. **Eleanor Farjeon:** 'Poetry' from *The Children's Bells* (OUP), 'The Quarrel' and 'There Isn't Time!' from *Silver Sand and Snow* (Michael Joseph). All poems © Eleanor Farjeon and reproduced by permission of David Higham Associates Ltd. **Max Fatchen:** 'Ruinous Rhymes' and 'Just Fancy That' © Max Fatchen, *Wry Rhymes for Troublesome Times*, Kestrel/Penguin 1983. **Rachel Field:** 'Something Told the Wild Geese' © Rachel Field reproduced by permission of Harvard University. **F. Scott Fitzgerald:** 'There Was an Orchestra' © F. Scott Fitzgerald reproduced by permission of David Higham Associates Ltd. **John Foster:** 'Four O'Clock Friday' © John Foster, reproduced by permission of the author. **Robert Frost:** 'The Road Not Taken' and 'The Secret Sits' from *The Poetry of Robert Frost* edited by Edward Connery Lathem, published by Jonathan Cape. Reprinted by permission of the Random House

Group Ltd. **Esther Valck Georges:** 'Alley Cat' from *Beauty of the Beast* (ed. J. Prelutsky, Knopf). **Nikki Giovanni:** 'poem for rodney' from *Spin a Soft Black Song, revised edition* by Nikki Giovanni, illustrated by George Martins. Copyright © 1971, 1985 by Nikki Giovanni. Reprinted by permission of Hill and Wang, a division of Farrar, Straus and Giroux, LLC. **David Greygoose:** 'It's Only the Storm' from *Language in Colour* (Belair). **Philip Gross:** 'Small Dawn Song' from *The All-Nite Cafe (Faber)* © Philip Gross, reprinted by permission of Faber and Faber Ltd. **Nicalás Guillén:** 'Hunger' from *Poetry Jump-Up* (Puffin). **David Harmer:** 'Divali' from *Let's Celebrate* (OUP). Reproduced by permission of the author. **John Hegley:** 'On Bonfire Night' from *Glad to Wear Glasses.* Reprinted by permission of PFD on behalf of John Hegley. Copyright © John Hegley. **Diana Hendry:** 'The Spare Room' reproduced by permission of Jenny Brown Associates on behalf of the author. **Adrian Henri**: 'Best Friends' from *The Phantom Lollipop Lady* (Methuen). Copyright © 1986 Adrian Henri. Reproduced by permission of the estate of Adrian Henri c/o Rogers, Coleridge & White Ltd., 20 Powis Mews, London W11 1JN. **Phoebe Hesketh:** 'Sally' from *Song of Sunlight* by Phoebe Hesketh, published by Chatto & Windus. Reprinted by permission of the Random House Group Ltd. **Russell Hoban:** 'Summer Goes' and 'Windows' from *Egg Thoughts and Other Frances Songs* (Faber). Copyright © Russell Hoban. Reproduced by permission of David Higham Associates Ltd. **Mary Ann Hoberman:** 'You Were the Mother Last Time' copyright © 1965 Mary Ann Hoberman from *Not Enough Beds for the Babies.* 'Yellow Butter' copyright © 1981 Mary Ann Hoberman and 'Combinations' copyright © 1976 Mary Ann Hoberman, both from *The Woman Who Had No Pajamas.* All used by permission of the Gina Maccoby Literary Agency. **Felice Holman:** 'Supermarket' © Felice Holman reproduced by permission of the author. **Libby Houston:** 'A Black Dot' © Libby Houston from *All Change* reproduced by permission of the author. **Ted Hughes:** 'My Grandpa' from *Meet My Folks* (Faber), 'Horrible Song' and 'Woodpecker' from *Collected Poems* (Faber) © The Estate of Ted Hughes, reprinted by permission of Faber and Faber Ltd. **Christopher Isherwood:** 'The Common Cormorant' © Christopher Isherwood. Reproduced by permission of the Estate of Christopher Isherwood. **Elizabeth Jennings:** 'Friends' and 'Holidays at Home' © Elizabeth Jennings from *The Secret Brother* (Macmillan) reproduced by permission of David Higham Associates Ltd. **T. H. Jones:** 'Advice to a Knight' © T. H. Jones from *The Colour of Cockcrowing* reproduced by permission of Madeleine Mitchell. **Jenny Joseph:** 'Running and Catching' and 'Looking at Pictures' copyright © Jenny Joseph, *All the Things I See*, Macmillan 2000. **Jackie Kay:** 'New Baby' and 'Names' copyright © Jackie Kay from *The Puffin Book of Utterly Brilliant Poetry.* Reprinted by permission of PFD (www.pfd.co.uk) on behalf of Jackie Kay. **Philip Larkin:** 'The Trees' from *Collected Poems* (Faber) © Philip Larkin, reprinted by permission of Faber and Faber Ltd. **Marian Lines:** 'Motorway' © Marian Lines. Reproduced by permission of the author. **Norman MacCaig:** 'An Ordinary Day' from *The Poems of Norman MacCaig* is reproduced by permission of Polygon, an imprint of Birlinn Ltd (www.birlinn.co.uk). **Lindsay MacRae:** 'The Babysitter' and 'Middle Child' from *How to Avoid Kissing Your Parents in Public* (Puffin, 2000) © Lindsay MacRae, 2000, 'Being in a Bad Mood' from *How to Make a Snail Fall in Love With You* (Puffin, 2003) © Lindsay MacRae, 2003, and 'Animal Rights' from *You Canny Shove Yer Granny Off a Bus* (Viking, 1995) © Lindsay MacRae, 1995. Reproduced by permission of Penguin Books Ltd. **Wes Magee:** 'What Is the Sun?' © Wes Magee from *The Witch's Brew and Other Poems.* Reproduced by permission of the author. **John Masefield:** 'Sea-Fever' reproduced by permission of The Society of Authors as the Literary Representative of John Masefield. **David McCord:** 'Mr Bidery's Spidery Garden' from *Mr Bidery's Spidery Garden* (Puffin, 1989) copyright © David McCord. Reproduced by permission of Chambers Harrap Publishers Ltd. **Roger McGough:** 'Sound Advice', 'New Poem', and 'sametimedotcom' from *Good Enough to Eat* by Roger McGough (© Roger McGough 2002); 'Fame' from *Nailing the Shadow* (© Roger McGough 1989); and 'First Day at School' from *In the Glassroom* (© Roger McGough 1976) are all reproduced by permission of PFD (www.pfd.co.uk) on behalf of Roger McGough. **Ian McMillan:** 'No Bread' © Ian McMillan. Reproduced by permission of the author. **Colin McNaughton:** 'The Garden's Full of Witches' © 1987 Colin McNaughton from *There's an Awful Lot of Weirdos in Our Neighbourhood* by Colin McNaughton. Reproduced by permission of Walker Books Ltd, London SE11 5HJ. **Spike Milligan:** 'Kids' and 'Said the General' © Spike Milligan, reprinted by kind permission of Spike Milligan Productions Ltd. **A. A. Milne:** 'Happiness' and 'Lines and Squares' from *When We Were Very Young* by A. A. Milne © The Trustees of the Pooh Properties. Published by Egmont UK Ltd London and used with permission. **Adrian Mitchell:** 'The Woman of Water' and 'A Speck Speaks' from *Nothingmas Day* copyright © 1984 by Adrian Mitchell (first published by Allison & Busby Ltd). Reproduced by kind permission of PFD (www.pfd.co.uk) on behalf of Adrian Mitchell. Adrian Mitchell Educational Health Warning! Adrian asks that none of his poems be used in connection with any examinations whatsoever! **John Mole:** 'Why Did the Chicken?' © John Mole from *The Mad Parrot's Countdown.* Reproduced by permission of the author. **Brian Morse:** 'Bye, Cat' from *Plenty of Time* copyright © Brian Morse. Reproduced by permission of the author c/o Rogers, Coleridge & White Ltd., 20 Powis Mews, London W11 1JN. **Brian Moses:** 'How Can I?' © Brian Moses from *Rice, Pie and Moses,* reproduced by permission of the author. **Ogden Nash:** 'The Tale of Custard the Dragon' , 'The Duck', and 'Song of the Open Road' from *Candy Is Dandy: The Best of Ogden Nash* (Andre Deutsch), copyright © Ogden Nash. Reprinted by permission of Andre Deutsch Limited. **Judith Nicholls:** 'Mary Celeste' © Judith Nicholls from *Midnight Forest* reproduced by permission of the author. **Grace Nichols:** 'Ar-a-rat' copyright © Grace Nichols 1991 and 'I Am the Rain' copyright © Grace Nichols 1984 reproduced with permission of Curtis Brown Group Ltd. **Alfred Noyes:** 'The Highwayman' reproduced by permission of The Society of Authors as the Literary Representative of Alfred Noyes. **Julie O'Callaghan:** 'High Life' from *Taking My Pen for a Walk* reproduced by permission of the author. 'My Life' from *Two Barks* reproduced by permission of Bloodaxe Books. 'Unhappy Whispers' and 'Whispering Leaves' from *The Book of Whispers* reproduced by permission of Faber and Faber Ltd. **Gareth Owen:** 'Jonah and the Whale' © Gareth Owen reproduced by permission of the author. **Brian Patten:** 'The Secret Rhyme for Orange' and 'Schoolitis' from

Thawing Frozen Frogs, 'Dear Mum' from *Juggling with Gerbils*, and 'A Small Dragon' from *Notes to the Hurrying Man* copyright © Brian Patten. Reproduced by permission of the author c/o Rogers, Coleridge & White Ltd., 20 Powis Mews, London W11 1JN. **Andrew Fusek Peters:** 'California Skateboard Park, 1977' taken from *Mad, Bad and Dangerously Haddock* by Andrew Fusek Peters, published by Lion Hudson plc, 2006. Copyright © Andrew Fusek Peters. Used with permission of Lion Hudson plc. **Jack Prelutsky:** 'Alphabet Stew' © Jack Prelutsky from *Alphabet Stew* (Random House). 'The Visitor' text copyright © 1978 by Jack Prelutsky. Used by permission of HarperCollins Publishers. **Kathleen Raine:** 'The Moment' from *Collected Poems* © Kathleen Raine. Reprinted by permission of Counterpoint Press, a member of Perseus Books Group. **James Reaney:** 'Lake Superior' from *Poems* (New Press) reproduced by permission of the author. **James Reeves:** 'W', 'Stones by the Sea', and 'Grim and Gloomy' from *Complete Poems for Children* by James Reeves (Heinemann) © James Reeves. Reprinted by permission of the James Reeves Estate. **Christopher Reid:** 'A Tent' from *All Sorts*. Reproduced by permission of Ondt & Gracehoper and the author. **Michael Richards:** 'The Magic Handbag' and 'What is Christmas?' from *Junk Mail* (OUP, 1993) reprinted by permission of Michael Harrison. **E. V. Rieu:** 'Sir Smashum Uppe' reproduced by permission of the Authors' Licensing and Collecting Society Ltd. **Michael Rosen:** 'I'm Just Going Out' by Michael Rosen from *Wouldn't You Like to Know* (© Michael Rosen 1977), and 'Father Says' and 'From the Winter Wind' by Michael Rosen from *Mind Your Own Business* (© Michael Rosen 1974) are reproduced by permission of PFD (www.pfd.co.uk) on behalf of Michael Rosen. **Vernon Scannell:** 'The Day That Summer Died' © Vernon Scannell from *Collected Poems*, reproduced by permission of the author. **Beatrice Schenk de Regniers:** 'Keep a Poem in Your Pocket' from *Something Special* by Beatrice Schenk de Regniers. Copyright © 1958, 1986 Beatrice Schenk de Regniers. Used by permission of Marian Reiner. **Ian Serraillier:** 'Anne and the Field-Mouse' © Estate of Ian Serraillier from *Happily Ever After* (OUP, 1963). Reprinted by permission of the Estate of Ian Serraillier. **Shel Silverstein:** 'The Farmer and the Queen' from *Where the Sidewalk Ends* by Shel Silverstein. Copyright © 1974, renewed 2002 Evil Eye, LLC. By permission of Edite Kroll Literary Agency Inc. 'Zebra Question' from *A Light in the Attic* by Shel Silverstein. Copyright © 1981 by Evil Eye Music, Inc. By permission of Edite Kroll Literary Agency Inc. **N. F. Simpson:** 'One of Our St Bernard Dogs is Missing' © N. F. Simpson. Copyright agent: Alan Brodie Representation Ltd, 6th Floor, Fairgate House, 78 New Oxford Street, London WC1A 1HB. info@alanbrodie.com. **Anthony Stuart:** 'Trying Places' reprinted by permission of Christopher Stuart-Clark. **Matthew Sweeney:** 'Cows on the Beach' and 'All the Dogs' from *The Flying Spring Onion* (Faber) © Matthew Sweeney, reprinted by permission of Faber and Faber Ltd. **Dylan Thomas:** 'Fern Hill' and 'The Song of the Mischievous Dog' from *Collected Poems* (Dent) reproduced by permission of David Higham Associates Ltd. **Nicole Townsend:** 'City Jungle' from *Rattling in the Wind* (CUP). **Steve Turner:** 'The Vegetables Strike Back' taken from *The Day I Fell Down the Toilet* by Steve Turner, published by Lion Hudson plc, 1996. Copyright © 1996 Steve Turner. Used with permission of Lion Hudson plc. **Judith Viorst:** 'That Old Haunted House' by Judith Viorst from *Sad Underwear and Other Complications*. Published by Atheneum Books for Young Readers (USA). An imprint of Simon & Schuster Children's Publishing Division. Text copyright © 1995 by Judith Viorst. Reprinted by permission of Lescher & Lescher, Ltd. All rights reserved. **Barrie Wade:** 'Truth' from *Conkers* reproduced by permission of the author. **John Walsh:** 'The Bully Asleep' from *The Truant* (Heinemann). **Colin West:** 'Reflections' © Colin West from *Between the Sun, the Moon and Me* reproduced by permission of the author. **William Carlos Williams:** 'Between Walls' from *Collected Poems* (Carcanet, 1987) by permission of Carcanet Press Limited. **Valerie Worth:** 'Chairs', 'Clock', and 'Mice' from *All the Small Poems and Fourteen More* by Valerie Worth. Copyright © 1987, 1994 by Valerie Worth. Reprinted by permission of Farrar, Straus and Giroux, LLC. **Kit Wright:** 'Me', 'Rabbiting On', and 'Sergeant Brown's Parrot' from *Rabbiting On* reproduced by permission from the author. 'Greedyguts' from *Hot Dog and Other Poems* by Kit Wright (Kestrel, 1981) © Kit Wright 1981 reproduced by permission of Penguin Books Ltd. **Judith Wright:** 'Legend' from *A Human Pattern: Selected Poems* (ETT imprint, Sydney 1996). Reproduced by permission of ETT imprint. **Benjamin Zephaniah:** 'Natural Anthem' and 'Good Hope' from *Funky Chickens* by Benjamin Zephaniah (Viking, 1996). Copyright © Benjamin Zephaniah, 1996. Reproduced by permission of Penguin Books Limited. 'Solidarity' from *Talking Turkeys* by Benjamin Zephaniah (Viking, 1994). Copyright © Benjamin Zephaniah, 1994. Reproduced by permission of Penguin Books Limited.

Although every effort has been made to trace and contact copyright holders before publication, this has not been possible in every case. If notified, the publisher will be pleased to rectify any errors or omissions at the earliest opportunity.